D1231671

KAISER WAKES
THE DOCTORS

Books by Paul de Kruif

OUR MEDICINE MEN

MICROBE HUNTERS

HUNGER FIGHTERS

SEVEN IRON MEN

MEN AGAINST DEATH

WHY KEEP THEM ALIVE?

THE FIGHT FOR LIFE

HEALTH IS WEALTH

KAISER WAKES THE DOCTORS

Book in Preparation

IMMORTALS OF TOMORROW

Kaiser Wakes the Doctors

PAUL DE KRUIF

NEW YORK

HARCOURT, BRACE AND COMPANY

This book is complete and unabridged.
It is manufactured in conformity with government regulations for saving paper.

TO RHEA AND MY MOTHER

ACKNOWLEDGMENT

This book had its initial spark in a little story, TOMORROW'S HEALTH PLAN—TODAY!, published in the May, 1943, issue of *The Reader's Digest*. That story is a condensation of the present historic effort of Henry Kaiser and California's doctors to bring maximum medical care within the reach of all the people, to keep medicine in the hands of the doctors and the people, and to keep medicine out of the hands of Government bureaucrats. For his patience, his great generosity, his understanding and his guidance in my small part in this adventure, best thanks to Mr. De Witt Wallace.

CONTENTS

KAISER WAKES
THE DOCTORS

CHAPTER 1

CONFESSION

THE BANGING, clanging, rhythmic flow of men and steel into a Liberty ship, complete from keel to launching within five days, is not the most epochal event at Henry Kaiser's shipyards. In today's cruel world you find a bit of the Sermon on the Mount in action there. In these days, grim with medical neglect, the genial giant Henry Kaiser acts as if the shipyard workers are a bit better than ordinary human beings. When they're hurt or when they're sick, every one of the 125,000 welders, riggers, flangers, down to the humblest laborers—all get unlimited medical care by expert groups of doctors in ultra-modern hospitals. It is far ahead of the medical treatment received by the majority of American citizens; it is better, on the whole, than that paid for at fancy prices by the lucky few of our upper economic brackets.

Of course medical care in certain industries has long been in existence, and in a few industries it is admirably complete. But what strikes you about Kaiser's medical mercy is its epic generosity. The shipbuilders, you understand, are a strange host not only of the healthy, but the

3

half-sick, the half-alive, the halt, the maimed, the partly blind. Thousands are 4-F's, rejects from the draft. Thousands are women not used to industry's strain. Thousands are those upon whose hearts and blood vessels the insidious deterioration of mid-life bears heavy. Many are old, even very old, and should not be trying to work any more at all. Yet all of them—and no questions asked!—are eligible to the mighty science and the tender kindness of Henry Kaiser's health plan.

This is outstanding: there are no preliminary medical examinations to rule out the unfit. There are no ifs, no buts, no embarrassing questions. They are not turned away because it is clear that they have had this or that chronic illness before they came to work for Kaiser. All are urged to enjoy this modern medical mercy without restrictions, without niggling exceptions, with no hard-hearted exclusions.

Yet Kaiser's health plan is in no sense charity. By a few cents daily deducted from their wages, if they want it deducted and they nearly all of them want it, these working men and women *prepay* their medical care so that it is no burden. But they do more than that. The sum, accumulating from their individual few cents a day, is rapidly paying off the building of the magnificent new hospitals that have risen near by with the same Kaiserish speed as that of the building of the ships.

So, under Henry Kaiser's guidance, it is the workers themselves who are building the model of a Mayo Clinic for the common man. Here where there is no money consideration between the sick man and his physician, you see a blueprint for group medical practice for the common man, for the powerful preventive medicine of our doctors for tomorrow.

This now is my confession. It was seeing Henry Kaiser's health plan in operation that has disturbed me, yes, shamed me at my failure to tell of other and earlier pioneering plans to bring medical care within the reach of everybody. I've dared to say that public health is the right of everybody. But for years I have been acting as if medical care was not *my* hot potato. As if you could have good public health without good medical care for everybody! In my dodging of this issue I have been especially to blame. As a reporter for the past 20 years I've been telling millions about new discoveries to ease their pain, to cure their formerly hopeless sickness, to save their lives. For myself and family there has been knowledge of where to go for this new powerful science. There has been wherewithal to pay the hospitals and the doctors. But meanwhile during all these years, plaints from medical have-nots have been pouring in on me in mounting thousands. Here is the sad burden of their story—

You tell us of this new hope for strength and life. But where do *we* find the hospitals and the doctors? And if we find them, where do *we* get the money we must pay?

The answers to the vast majority of these pathetic letters could not be satisfactory. So here now is my blame. It has been my pride to be democratic, to believe in the common man, and to resent it when the underdog is shoved around. But what have I done to fight for the medical underdogs, the medical have-nots? Their numbers are far greater than those who in the great depression were ill-clothed, ill-housed, ill-fed. Their state of grim medical want has not even lifted with the waning of the great depression. And when it comes to resenting people's being pushed around, what pushing around is so heartless, so Nazi-cruel, as the neglect of men and women, children and babies who are in pain, and feeble, and in danger of dying —while science does exist to save them?

I must face it: my conduct has not only been far from that of the Good Samaritan, it has been worse than that of the Levite who preceded him, who merely passed by on the other side of the road from the dying man. But I have passed by, after rousing hopes in God knows how many thousands of sick people. I've made them yearn for medical care that should be theirs, for medical science that, *in the present economic organization of medical practice,* is too often not obtainable.

What could I have done? I could have investigated the sound and practical medical care plans that have existed long before this new brilliant industrial plan of Henry Kaiser's. These plans have lacked the magic lavishness and that curious religious element of complete generosity that distinguishes the medical mercy enjoyed by the shipbuilders, that's true. But even so, these previously existing plans had power to bring better medicine within reach of many more millions of Americans.

Why did I hesitate? I am supposed to like a fight. For years I've heard, never listening too intently, of brave beginnings, of struggles, of defeats, of the slow growth of co-operative associations of prospective sick people who want to stay healthy. Like any other form of insurance, these prepaid medical care plans have spread the risk, so that sick people's unbearable financial burden might be shared by those who are well. But here was the catch: these prepaid medical care plans were *medically* not popular: it was the organization of the doctors themselves who opposed them. Physicians who dared to join groups of people in organizing prepaid medical care were many of them made outcasts from medical respectability. They were kicked around by their medical societies and kicked out of them.

Now what I failed to do was to go deep into the rights and wrongs of these obscure battles. Years before the Supreme Court of the United States of America ruled unanimously that it was legal for people to band together with doctors to prepay for their medical care, I had been asked my private opinion on this grim question by an Attorney General of the United States. I was like the disciple, Thomas, in the Bible story. I doubted, I said I didn't know. I remained content with official medical explanations that this prepaid medicine was *unethical*. Not stopping to ask what, indeed, is this medical ethics. Not examining into official dark hints that the medical care given by these co-operatives was not so hot.

Let's face it: all these years it seemed safer for me to stay on the sidelines. Let's be blunt about it: in me there has been a bit of the rabbit. One hundred thousand doctors could not be wrong. Where I was wrong was in failing to find out whether the doctors' organizations really represented all of the one hundred thousand doctors.

7

CHAPTER 2

THEN CAME HENRY KAISER

Now in November, 1942, I met Henry J. Kaiser. He had just made nationwide headlines at a hearing of a U. S. Senate Committee in Washington. The subject of the hearing was the disturbing disproportion between the number of doctors serving the Army and the number remaining to treat the ills of civilians. Of course our soldiers should have the best medical care; nobody denied it. But now, by the end of 1942, the Army had nearly one doctor for every hundred soldiers—while in many rural and industrial areas there remained only one physician for every three, four, five, even seven thousands of people. It was against the dire threat of this dearth of doctors that Henry J. Kaiser was protesting.

Mind you, Kaiser had seen to it that his own shipyard workers did have doctors, groups of highly trained physicians giving medical care on a prepaid plan that was in reach of all of them. Here is what struck me about Henry Kaiser's Senate testimony: that, though his own workers were taken care of, he should take the time and trouble

8

to plead the cause of the millions of America's medical underdogs who were needlessly sick, who might needlessly die, many of them for lack of medical care. This was front page news, though that angle of it was not noticed by any newspaper. Could it possibly be that the nation's master builder had in him a touch of the Good Samaritan?

This led to my meeting Kaiser in late November, 1942, in New York City. He was a massive man who, curiously, moved as fast as a welterweight prize-fighter. His jaw was heavy, his mouth wide and firm—just right for a movie director's idea of the super-builder that he was. But his eyes, in contrast, were extraordinarily kind. He was monolithic. He seemed physically and in his thought and spirit to be built of some curious kind of protoplasmic granite. You knew immediately that it would be useless to try to chip pieces off Henry Kaiser, to make him compromise, to whittle him down to less than his epic size. He would build more boats, and faster than any other builder, or go bust trying to build them. He'd build cargo airplanes if there weren't enough boats for victory. About medical care he was fanatic. Not about good medical care for the best people. Nor about the best medical care for deserving people. But for the highest possible scientific medical care for the rich and middle and the poor, for saints and sinners, for everybody.

This shook me, excited me. Who had ever before found such a religion in a man who was at the same time the country's production genius and its non-military hero? Mind you, Kaiser did not pretend to have discovered that proper medical care was good for the production of his workers. He knew that other industrialists—though a minority—had doctored and hospitalized their employees when they were sick. The Southern Pacific and Sante Fe Railroads had long fostered medical care plans. The same was true of the Consolidated Edison Company, of New York, the Tennessee Coal and Iron Company, of Birmingham, Alabama, the Endicott-Johnson Company, of Binghamton, New York, and others. But, in contrast to Henry Kaiser, the executives of these companies were not on record as burning with the will to spread the boon of good medical care to all the workers of the nation.

Indeed, certain industrial companies looked upon their medical care as primarily practical, not as religious. Dr. Franz Goldmann, of the Yale University School of Medicine, has recently published a study of four of the best and most complete medical care plans long operative in four companies. In summary, writes Dr. Goldmann, these companies considered "that their expenditure for medical care constitutes a sound and profitable investment." In his valuable article Dr. Goldmann was not allowed to publish the names of the companies which had so laudably pioneered in this neglected field.

But here this morning was Henry Kaiser—working far beyond the limit of an ordinary man's strength on gigantic projects to win the war—dropping these preoccupations and telling me that he was first of all going to put his project of good prepaid group medical care—for everybody—across to industry, to the medical profession, to the nation. Here he was, way out in front there, really alone, ahead of any prominent physician, far ahead of any politician or statesman, of any public-spirited citizen. In this he was certainly far ahead of his time and so much of a visionary that he would have disturbed me—if I hadn't known that here was a man with a curious trick of making wild dreams come true.

He was at this moment writing a speech to the National Association of Manufacturers. Their leaders—gloomy and frantic with forebodings about the awful future of business—had begged him to give them a message of cheer about what management could do to save the post-war world. He had a draft of this proposed speech on his desk. Now from this he began to expound purple passages and perorations. They were a challenge to industry, and marked him as a new and curious kind of industrial prophet. He was strangely unworried about our gigantic national debt. He proposed that we use the bonds—that were the reverse side of this horrible debt—in the hands of our American millions, as pledges for the purchase of the goods of the now possible terrific production of goods for life and peace, the moment the production of goods for death and war should be no longer necessary.

Again, in his proposals, he was ahead of his time. He insisted we must begin to build the post-war world, *now*, in the midst of war, and long before the coming armistice. To stave off the collapse of employment inevitable when our millions shall have done with fabricating flying fortresses, tanks, airplane carriers, and cannon, Kaiser demanded mobilization, *right now*, of the scientists, engineers, designers, physicians, public healthmen to build the world of tomorrow. And again, in regard to just what this building should be, Kaiser was a revolutionary. It was not only for the building of super-highways, of millions of houses, of new cheap automobiles and airplanes that industry should now launch out boldly. But on a par with these projects he demanded building of thousands of hospitals and health centers—*for the nation's essential medical care.*

Among the plans of industrialists and politicians this was unprecedented.

In our conversation it became clear that Henry Kaiser, in his personal experience with the medical care of his own workers, had made observations undreamed of by men of science, by medical administrators, by public healthmen, or by political leaders. He kept talking in terms that were positively Utopic, about beautiful hospitals, splendid laboratories, complete hospital, medical, and laboratory care generous beyond even Soviet dreams, but now practicable and potentially within the reach of everybody. His men were beginning to get that sort of thing at his Richmond, California, and Vancouver, Washington, shipyards, he said.

"But such hospitals," I protested, "they'd have to be built by vast government appropriations, and I understand you're opposed to big Government handouts."

Then he uncovered one of the secret weapons that he was sure would bring us victory in America's coming fight for nationwide health. "We won't need Government handouts," he explained, with fire in his eyes and a slow smile. "Our medical chief, Dr. Garfield, has proved at Coulee Dam, and is proving now at Richmond shipyards, that if you properly organize and distribute the burden of payment for the best kind of hospital and medical care, the hospitals will quickly amortize themselves; *they'll pay themselves off!"*

That was going to be his first challenge to the manufacturers, he said. They wouldn't mind managing medical care, if stockholders were not forced to fork out additional money. Then, with that lightning-like movement of his, so strange in so massive a man, he fumbled through his manuscript with quick, heavy, eager fingers, and read—

"Will the manufacturers now dare to organize, finance, and manage medical centers in every industrial community, where medical service could be purchased on an insurance basis at a cost which would bring not only the skill and facilities but all the advantages of research within the reach of the common man?"

"The common man!" Henry Kaiser was going to throw that phrase in the teeth of the manufacturers, most of whom seemed not sympathetic with the vision of Vice President Henry A. Wallace.

Kaiser's boldness stirred me, and yet, the imps of doubt and fear, that had kept me from writing in the service of the crusade for the spread of medical care, now whispered to me that Kaiser was indulging in fairy godmother dreams, in wishful thinking. Even if the manufacturers would go for his plan, seeing as how good medical care would lower their man-hours, vastly raise their production, even so could Kaiser convince the doctors? The physicians whose voices are most powerful in organized medicine are specialists who make good livings on fees not from the common but from the *un*common man. "These specialists largely guide the medical rank and file. Will they be interested?" I asked.

Henry Kaiser brushed aside this query. After all the rich specialists, though medico-politically powerful, were in the minority. Kaiser was ready to appeal to the medical rank and file, especially the younger physicians. He had it clear that, under the individualism of private practice, all was not too secure with the bread and butter of scores of thousands of little doctors. And then, too, immediately post-war, there'd be scores of thousands of young physicians coming back to civil life, who'd had a taste of group medical care, of giving the most scientific medical care to millions, with no consideration of the cost of it—and on salaries which made their own lives secure.

"Yes, but isn't your prepaid industrial medicine really socialized medicine in disguise?" I asked Kaiser. "The propaganda of their leaders has made socialized medicine the worst bogey for the mass of physicians, old and young."

He answered me by reaching for his speech again, fumbling through it rapidly to find this passage—

"If the doctors fear socialized medicine, if industry is anxious about the widening powers of the State, why not venture *now,* boldly, into the activity that will forestall the super-planners in their schemes to direct medical service into the channels of distributive bounty?"

Kaiser explained he was at one with medical leaders in their horror of tax-supported, government medicine, of health by government handout. "There's got to be an end to this handout business. We've got to make everything we build and use—pay its way," he said.

As I listened to this builder with the heavy jaw, the determined mouth and the strangely luminous eyes, it became clear to me how completely he had broken with past tradition. Industrialists have frequently been lavish with their medical and other "charities" as witness Mr. Rockefeller. Rich specialist physicians are famous not only for their thumping fees from those who can pay; they are proud, too, of their charitable work in the university and city and county hospitals. But such respectable philanthropies were anathema to Kaiser. He hated charity. He kept repeating that it was his experience that the ordinary man—if he's healthy—wants to work.

"When a fellow's making mistakes, when he's soldiering on the job, how do we know whether he's well? Isn't he failing because he's sick?" asked Kaiser. He kept assuring me that the mass of men and women wanted to work and wanted to pay their doctors.

For a last time he reached for his manuscript and from it rehearsed his exhortation to the industrialists—

"Can they (the manufacturers) assure labor the opportunity to continue to earn so that every man may pay his own way . . . so that the tolls from the highways and bridges will amortize their costs; so that the fees from organized medical centers will provide profits which will be available, not only for extensions, improvements, and research, but for the adequate compensation of medical service (the doctors)?"

When for long you've despaired of finding a light to

guide you, and when you then suddenly find that leading beacon—and here it was in Henry Kaiser—then you're in the clouds, you feel as if you're walking on air, and everything seems possible. Henry Kaiser was a kindly giant, brushing aside all the impossibles with which faint-hearted men have put the dead hand on human progress. That November morning his enthusiasm made it all seem easy. Now the sick would take up their beds and walk. Now the dying would wake up, like Lazarus. Now doctors would become as Hippocrates and Aesculapius. Now scientists would have power that would make Semmelweis and Pasteur turn over in their graves.

Yet, while Henry Kaiser stirred me to drop all else and follow him and let my comfortable living go hang, if necessary, to tell America this story, yet at the back of my head those imps of doubt and caution were whispering.

"Don't let him take you in," they murmured. "Remember that your life is justly said to be a series of enthusiasms. Remember, Kaiser is only a dam builder, a boat builder. He is not a doctor. What fools you is that he is riding the crest now. He's like Henry Ford in his great days. Kaiser feels he can do anything. Remember Ford's peace ship. Was that practical?"

My imps kept whispering all the cautions that guard the reputations of careful men, of men of little faith, of small men who ride in upon the results of the blood and sweat and toil of pioneers. Why not hedge now? Why not take my stand with the wise men who make their reputations by their "I-told-you-so" when bold men, like Kaiser, reach too far, try too much, and then are discredited with their dreams turned to dust.

Kaiser had clairvoyance. He seemed to sense enthusiasm struggling in my head with those imps of doubt and caution. As I rose to go, he chuckled.

"You see," he said, "I'm not kidding myself about this present crest of the wave. Today people on the street spot me as if I was some movie actor. I'm riding the wave now, but I know it won't be long before it hits the rocks." His face was sad. Then he smiled. "But, by God," he said, "while I'm up on the crest I'm going to try to start things; I'm going to try to get a few things done."

I knew that this good prepaid group medical care for everybody was the toughest job that Kaiser had ever tackled, far more formidable than helping to finish the Grand Coulee Dam a year and a half ahead of schedule, far tougher than building boats fantastically faster than any had ever been built in history. The tough part of it would not be convincing the industrialists: they didn't mind stronger manpower. The tough job wasn't convincing the bankers: they would love financing hospitals and health centers if these were a sound investment. And the people—no, 135,000,000 American people would not mind prepaid medical care, for which they all would equitably pay, which would relieve them of their pain, sickness, misery and needless death.

No, the tough part of it would be to convince the doctors. They were the keymen. The industrialists could go to our leading doctors, who might tell them that Henry Kaiser's health plan was hooey. The bankers could go to the big physicians who might shake their heads and say it was wonderful, but alas not medically sound. And the people? Alas, they were not organized, they were inarticulate. The voice of the common man could not reach the doctors.

Without the enthusiastic co-operation of our nation's physicians, Kaiser's health plan was so much moonshine. The odds were heavy against his getting that co-operation. Yet, at the end of that morning, I conquered my imps of doubt and fear and caution and decided to follow him come what might. I determined to follow him because it was so plain that he was a man of tomorrow. For me he was a new type of industrial leader because he was tough but kindly. It was this warmth for people that illuminated his dam-building, his boat-building, his new projects for great transcontinental highways, portable houses, automobiles and airplanes for everybody, and health centers, all with a new epic adventurous glow. Kaiser did not think of labor as a commodity. He did not regard workers as expendable. Here he was not only talking but acting as if the 250,000 men and women who worked for him were not mere producing units, not robots, but human. It is true that he was naïve and in a way old-fashioned. He kept saying he knew all people wanted was to be happy. But he was advanced. He had dedicated himself to the proposition that to be happy, the common man must first of all be healthy.

And it was plain to me that this was more than theory. At his West Coast shipyards, Kaiser had made a beginning of putting happiness through health to mass experiment.

He believed that what he had begun for more than 100,-
000 shipbuilders could be done, too, for smaller industries, for communities rural as well as industrial.

Now he did not ask me to take all this on faith. "Maybe
there are bugs in this health plan," he said. "Why don't
you come out to the coast and try to find out what's wrong
with it? The hospitals, the medical staff, how the workers
feel about it—all of it is open to you. You can see the
books and accounts, the whole set-up. You can talk to the
doctors of the San Francisco Bay area who've looked us
over. Ask them. I don't know much about the details,
myself. Why don't you come out and go over the details
of the whole plan with Dr. Garfield? He's our medical
chief. He originated it and is responsible for all of it."

That morning with this Western giant—strong, simple,
gentle, and not proud—made me ashamed to be afraid.

CHAPTER 3

THE DESERT DOCTOR

ARRIVING in San Francisco on the yellow streamliner ten days after this first momentous meeting with Henry Kaiser, I expected to find Dr. Garfield a go-getting, free-swinging, stem-winding big man in the Kaiser manner. Kaiser had told me of the speed with which his medical chief had met the terrible medical emergency of the avalanche of workers into the West Coast shipyards just after Pearl Harbor. Against the difficulty of the freezing of critical building materials, Garfield had built a group of first aid stations and a Field Hospital at the Richmond, California, yards. He had built the Permanente Hospital at Oakland. He had built the modern beautiful Northern Permanente Hospital and first aid stations at the yards at Vancouver, Washington. For these institutions he had assembled a staff of 90 skilled physicians in the very months when civilian America was being denuded of doctors for the armed forces. All this he had accomplished in six months in 1942. And in less than 10 months he had got his prepaid health plan into smooth operation with 60,000 workers already voluntarily subscribing to it and 40,000 more raring to get into it. About this achievement there seemed more than a touch of Kaiserish magic.

So I had pictured Garfield as a sort of replica of Henry Kaiser. But now to that Paul Bunyan builder the slender, mild-mannered Garfield turned out to be a contrast. Kaiser you'd spot instantly out of millions. He was known to workers, taxi-drivers, bankers, manufacturers, men and women on the street—a national figure. Kaiser had the looks of the trail-blazer that he was. You expected him, looking at him, to have a vision of a splendid new world of tomorrow rising from the ruins of the lost world of today. Being with Kaiser, you knew he'd have an up-thrusting dream of humanity coming alive post-war through work, health, and peace. But Garfield? At our first meeting I was let down by the looks of the young man who had demonstrated to Henry Kaiser that this dream of a healthy nation was possible, practical.

Garfield was a man whom you'd not pick out of the human mass as a leader. He was dapper in his dress. His lean face was finely chiseled, a model to tempt a sculptor. His eyes were hard to fathom because they looked at you through very narrow slits, like the eyes of a man who has lived long in mountain, ocean, or desert sun. He was serious, yet smiled easily, and then you could hardly see his eyes at all. You felt reliability in his face under its thick, red, curly hair. His movements were so slow and easy that it was hard to believe he could have organized the medical care of the great Kaiser worker army in such a fantastically short time as he had done it. He was quiet and spoke in a hesitant drawl. He seemed bashful and there was nothing aggressive, energetic, or fanatical about him on the surface. It was obvious that he was no salesman in the American success story manner.

In short, to me, Garfield was the final exposure of the phoniness of the art of our movie directors who cast men for type. Outwardly he seemed only a nice, very considerate, anonymous young man a little too concerned about how he wore his clothes, who might have inherited wealth, who was anything but the health plan pioneer that Henry Kaiser had told me that he was. Where was Garfield's drive?

Answering my bombardment of questions about his work, Garfield was clear-cut in his drawling answers. It was apparent that he was no double-talker, that he was honest. When not sure on a given point, he was quick to say, "I don't know." He was modest and surprised that I had come all the way to the West Coast on a pilgrimage to see his health plan. He seemed not at all sure that what he had accomplished at Kaiser's shipyards could be expanded—according to the bold plan of Kaiser himself—to medical care for the whole nation. About his prepaid group medical care Garfield at first seemed to have no such wide-swinging vision. He kept stressing the antagonism of certain elements of the doctors' organization to a plan that would so revolutionize the doctors' practices.

Garfield admitted that his medical care was good, was ahead of that of the nation as a whole, yet he was careful to point out that his plan was a long way from perfect. He kept explaining the many wonderful projects in preventive medicine, medical science, and group medical teamwork that were still lacking in his medical care of the Kaiser workers. He was in his mild way disgusted that he was giving this medical mercy only to the workers, not yet to their families. The expansion of the Kaiser shipbuilding army had been too terrific to let him attempt family care. Wasn't it a cruel thing to care for the workers but not their wives and children? But he hadn't the hospital facilities, and why didn't Mr. Kaiser help him get them—now? But on the other hand, why try it? Wouldn't the doctors of the San Francisco Bay region gang up to stop him if he tried it?

About this injustice Garfield was impatient in a quietly savage way. There was a hint of the pioneer about him: he was and would be permanently dissatisfied with any accomplishment. He was truly unworldly despite his urbane manner and his dress. He seemed to be always peering with those slit-like gray eyes toward a future where the mighty power of modern medical science would be for all, for the least of God's human creatures. That vision, expressed in a low key, was the first hint of Garfield's unspectacular genius.

Garfield was most satisfactory as a teacher of modern medical care because he was candid, explicit about difficulties and because he had a photographic memory. Quickly he showed me there was no magic about his rapid development of the health plan for the Kaiser workers. This outwardly fantastic medical achievement was natural because it was the result of nine years of medical care experimentation under strange and hard conditions. The only miracle was that Henry Kaiser had happened to find Garfield, to see in him the innovator that he was.

Garfield—with a vision of the new death-fighting possibilities of group medical teamwork—had begun his experiments in modern medical care as a lonewolf in the southern California desert. He had graduated from the excellent University of Iowa Medical School and then had migrated to the modern Los Angeles County Hospital, where the lucky poor people of the region get medical science better, on the average, than that of the middle or even the upper economic brackets. Here Garfield, during his years of service as an intern and a surgical resident, had it burned into him *why* the treatment of the poor man, the "medically indigent," is so superior. He began to understand the new power of medical science—when this is practiced by groups of doctors expert in the various medical disciplines, all of them assembled under one hospital roof. Here in the early 1930's Garfield became a quiet but fierce rebel against the horse-and-buggy medicine still so widespread in the nation.

He saw that the good old family doctor—God bless him —was a holdover from times before there was medical science, from days that now should be dead. Hardly more than a generation ago, the family doctor was a complete walking medical and surgical unit. He carried everything he knew in his head, and all his death-fighting weapons in a battered bag. His hospital was the patient's home. His operating room was the kitchen. His laboratory science was limited largely to boiling a tube of urine over a little sink in a cubby-hole adjacent to his office. There were no x-rays. There was no blood chemistry that now so brilliantly detects the early and still curable stages of what may turn out to be fatal sickness. His microscope—if the horse-and-buggy doctor owned one—was seldom used, and was kept under a bell jar to make the office look scientific. But now during Garfield's own life-time scientific medicine had blossomed. The field of medical knowledge became so immense that no one man could master all of it. The hospital, with its laboratories, x-rays, and operating rooms, was no longer a final refuge or a house of last resort. It had become the general headquarters of medicine, and the day-to-day workshop of the physician.

Yet this galled Garfield: that the majority of our doctors still practiced their medicine outside these workshops, or only performed their healing art in them part time, or incidentally. Their offices, far removed from the modern hospital, were still their G.H.Q.'s. It was as if fine automobile mechanics would do most of the fixing of your car with a screw-driver, monkey-wrench, and pair of pliers in their own backyards; and only occasionally insist that your motor trouble should have all the advantages of an up-to-date garage.

The practice of medicine, to paraphrase Michael Davis, remained horse-and-buggy for the immense majority of Americans who came vertically into a doctor's office. It was streamlined only for the well-to-do who could go to the Mayo Clinic, or for the poor man who went horizontally into a good county or city general hospital.

For Garfield good medicine meant group medicine centralized and streamlined under one clinic and hospital roof. This meant specialization, of necessity. No matter what your inborn genius for doctoring, you, as one man, couldn't in addition to your wonderful bedside manner, your hand-holding, your fevered-brow-soothing, your primitive pain-killing and physicking—also have at your finger tips blood chemistry, bacteriology, x-ray technique, and be skilled at removing safety pins from the air-tubes of babies and tumors from grown-up people's brains. Et cetera.

Finishing his residency in the Los Angeles County Hospital, Sidney Garfield began by being bitterly disappointed. He wanted to join a group of specialists. He wanted to teamwork with them, using his superb surgical skill and training. This was in the deep depression of the early 1930's and there was no place to go and he was faced with hanging out his shingle to wait for patients who would be terribly slow in coming, with the skill of his surgeon's hands unused, and rusting. It is true he might have taken a minor surgical teaching job in the University of Southern California Medical School. But instead his independent lonewolf's restlessness, a low-keyed adventurousness, drove him out of the possibility of such snug obscurity into the obscurity of industrial medical practice in the drouth and heat of the California desert.

So in 1933 Sidney Garfield launched out as a sort of desert-rat doctor, to take care of men who had next to no money in a hot dusty region never meant by God for human activity or habitation. In this land where the hot dust turns bitter in your mouth, the Los Angeles Aqueduct was being built to carry the pure water of the mountains to that city's millions. Along a 190-mile stretch between the little town of Indio and the Parker Dam site, 5000 men worked, frizzled in the hellish heat, got hurt, were sick, and had no medical care at all. Under the State of California's industrial compensation insurance law, when they were hurt in accidents they had to be carted all the way to Los Angeles. If they were not badly enough hurt, they got to the hospital alive. When they took sick, even fatally, it was just too bad. Garfield knew that 90 per cent of workmen's incapacity is not due to industrial injuries but to their just being plain sick, like clergymen or bankers or any other easy-living people. Only workmen get sick *more* often.

Medically, these 5000 prospective patients were among the folks God forgot.

Here now at the hellish little town of Desert Center, midway on the great Aqueduct project, Garfield set himself up—it was gallant and a bit pathetic—as a one man medical group to mend broken bones, repair smashed muscles, heal pneumonias, remove gangrenous appendixes, treat cancers, save men from the deadly threat of heat stroke. He became the lone doctor for this far-flung working-stiff army of the medically neglected.

CHAPTER 4

ARE PATIENTS HUMAN

BEINGS?

GARFIELD had saved $2500. On this he went seriously into debt to build a little 12-bed hospital at Desert Center. It cost much more than it should have, when you bear in mind that this Aqueduct construction would be no more than a four-year project, and that Garfield's only patients would be Aqueduct workmen. But this was just the point: the hospital was expensive because Garfield had a conviction that even working-stiffs are human beings. It was notorious among workingmen that the industrial wards in most hospitals are not as comfortable, as elegant, or as safe as the private hospital pavilions that house humanity's bon ton. In fact industrial wards have a nickname among hurt men who go to them. They are called "the butcher shop."

Dr. Garfield had his own notion about what kind of places all hospitals should be. He bore in mind that today's hospitals are direct descendants of the poorhouses

28

of the past, and that, with not too many exceptions, they still bear the stigma of what society thought good enough for its under-dogs and have-nots. Garfield started off, mind you, not as a reformer or social do-gooder, but on the deep-held hunch that the surroundings of any sick man are precisely as much a part of his treatment as the gleaming knife with which he's slit open, or the powerful serum with which you try to slay his microbes, or the quality of the x-ray with which you try to diagnose his sickness.

For our desert doctor, kindness cured, as well as cold science.

He knew that congested wards, devoid of privacy, and drab and stinky, are no part of kindness. This, you say, was no discovery of Garfield's. This would be agreed to by any good doctor. But where Garfield was a bit in advance was in his quaint belief that even a tunnel man, a concrete worker, realizes beautiful and comfortable surroundings, and reacts to them physically. . . . Here was a basic part of Sidney Garfield's medicine: any human being high or low or rich or poor can stand the gaff of bad environment when healthy. It's when *any* human being is hurt, or sick and full of toxins and down with energy at ebb tide—then of all times the surroundings should be most beautiful, most gentle.

So now, 1933, building his little desert hospital, Garfield went deep into debt trying to turn it into a little heaven. The building was pleasantly decorated inside, with a blend of colors easy to the eye. The bed linen would not have offended the body of a movie queen. The blankets matched the decorations, and were of the quality you'd

find in a luxury hotel. Against the glare of the desert sun
the eyes of the sick people were protected by the then
expensive and new-fangled Venetian blinds. Against the
hellish desert heat—bad enough for a well man—the sick
men were guarded by a complete air-conditioning system.
(This innovation is still hard to find in the finest hospitals
in big cities today; it's still considered too expensive.)
Boredom as well as hot uncomfortable stinking surroundings—being fed up with just lying there trying to get well
—this too checks the fight back up toward health. Garfield
installed radios, and provided good reading for the patients.

All beauty aids recovery, and Garfield's nurse was easy
for the men to look at.

This historic little desert hospital was more than merely
a pleasant place to go when you were sick. Its technical
equipment was the last word in science, the best Garfield
could buy. It contrasted—again to the astonishment of the
men—with that of the crude hospitals, those abattoirs they
had so feared and detested on other construction projects.
There was a good operating room, gleaming modern sterilizers, a small but up-to-date laboratory, a fine x-ray in-
stallation. It was a miniature modern city hospital fantastic in this desert.

The sick men loved it. By the desert grapevine all up
and down the 190 miles of the Aqueduct project the word
of this astounding house of refuge for men hurt or in pain
went out to the 5000 far-flung workmen. Not only hurt
men, but sick men—and they did not have to be so very
sick—flocked to the hospital; for the word flashed around

that here was a doc that didn't turn a guy away. Yet Garfield was troubled in his medical conscience. He realized that these fine facilities were only one part of what should be the total scientific mercy for this desert army of the medically neglected. Garfield missed terribly the team of specialists, x-ray and laboratory men, the modern medical machine of which he had been a cog at the Los Angeles County Hospital. Out here he had had to be that whole group, in one. Upon smashed skulls of workmen he did operations that should only have been undertaken by a brain surgeon. With his x-ray he attempted diagnoses that should have been done only by a radiologist.

He was loaded with debt, struggling to get started, able to build this tiny Mayo Clinic but unable to afford to hire the men to man it. He had only himself, one nurse, a laundress, and a cook to staff his little institution. He worked day and night, pinch-hitting for the nurse, the cook, and even for the laundress washing his patients' linen. And alas! When dog-tired, even then it was hard to sleep, haunted as he was by the red figures on his ledger.

You see, at Los Angeles County Hospital Garfield had helped to give medical mercy to poor people who did not have to pay. The best group medical care was theirs, for charity. But here his patients were men who had jobs, who should pay for their medical care. Now here was the rub: modern medical care has become too expensive for the ordinary workingman, even for the middle class salaried man, even for the small businessman to pay for, *as an individual,* when he's sick. And Garfield at the same time had in him more than a bit of the philosophy of the great

Russian, Lenin, whose watchword was: "To hell with charity."

Garfield was no more horse-and-buggy in his medical economics than he was in his medical science. He knew full well that the answer to the danger of sickness is precisely the same as the answer to the danger of flood, or cyclone, or fire, or death itself. The common sense answer is to spread the risk. The well must help to pay for those who are sick. The answer lay in one word: insurance. So at the very beginning he tried to start a health plan. He figured that a mere nickel a day, deducted from the wages of those 5000 men, would keep him going. That, plus a certain amount of money he'd earn from the workmen's compensation insurance companies for taking care of the men's industrial accidents and injuries. But here was the devil of it: The Aqueduct construction along that hot 190 miles was participated in by 15 separate construction companies. It was more than one man could do, to be physician, surgeon, x-ray and laboratory man, part time nurse, cook, and laundryman, collection agent, and at the same time salesman for prepaid medical care.

So in the first months in the desert Garfield had only 500 men from one construction company voluntarily kicking in their nickel a day. And, as for the industrial accident cases, he had to wrangle with the insurance companies for the fees for every treatment and operation. Now here was his dilemma. All up and down the Aqueduct word had spread of the swell guy this doc was, the fine little hospital he had, and the good care he gave you. Day and night, from all the companies, men would come in smashed up by cave-ins, bashed up by motor accidents, comatose from heat stroke, hot and with the labored breathing of pneumonia. He took them all in. He gave them the best care in his power. It ran up into a lot of money. Then, when he rendered his doctor and hospital bills, they couldn't or they wouldn't or they simply didn't pay. It galled him to keep dunning them. And the men? Just as they deeply appreciated this fine medical care, just so they resented the bills Garfield had to present them.

Garfield had to face this: there is something evil about money business between the doctor and the sick man. Did the Good Samaritan render a bill for his work of mercy; did Christ himself expect a fee for his laying on of hands? . . .

But meanwhile for Garfield there loomed the specter of the sheriff. Yet, before the first year of his experiment was over, his dark financial skies began to lighten, and for a reason that Garfield himself had not at all foreseen. Help came to him from the contractors, the men's employers. They'd stop into Garfield's little Desert Center Hospital. What was this? Who'd ever seen such an institution on any construction project? "Gee, you've got a swell little place here!" That was the tenor of their exclamations of surprise.

Now Garfield saw his chance. "I'm taking care of all your sick men. But they don't pay me. I'm not turning any of them away. If you could get them to kick in a nickel a day from their pay, on a health plan, I could make it go." So he urged them, persistent, in his low-keyed hesitant drawl.

It was not Garfield, who was anything but a salesman, it was his beautiful little hospital that sold the employers. By the end of the first year, thanks to the help of the employers and their superintendents and managers, 95 per cent of all the men of 14 out of the 15 companies up and down the Aqueduct project were paying their nickel a day, voluntarily, allowing it to be deducted from their wages. At the same time by a shrewd stroke, Garfield simplified his collection of fees for the medical care of the industrial accident cases. He persuaded the workmen's compensation insurance companies to pay him a flat rate, a percentage of all the premiums they took in from the contracting companies. First it was 10 per cent; later this amount was hiked to 17½ per cent of their premiums, when the insurance companies were made to realize how Garfield's excellent care of the men was putting money in the insurance companies' pockets.

Now money began to roll in without his having to fight to collect it.

By the end of 1933 he began to see his way out of his financial morass. Now he began assembling a staff of good young doctors, well trained in medicine, and placed them not only in the hospital but at first aid stations built at different points along the Aqueduct building project. And now, no longer threatened by the bailiff, Garfield began experimenting with another basic principle of good medical care. It was as important—and as little practiced—as the beauty and comfort of his desert hospital.

This new principle was that the medical, surgical, and hospital care of any hurt or sick man *must be limitless.*

There shouldn't be a choice between some medical care and medical care that is complete and unrestricted up to the maximum of the science and facilities available. So now there was no limit imposed by any sick or hurt man's pocketbook upon the time he could stay in the Desert Hospital. The limit was imposed by his complete recovery, or death. Garfield and his doctors, puzzled by the baffling sickness of a patient, didn't have to stint that patient on blood tests or blood chemistry determinations, didn't have to say: If your financial traffic would stand it, we might be able to find out what's the matter with you. When Garfield was in doubt about a fractured pelvis or a damaged brain, the high cost of x-ray plates didn't step in to put a dead hand upon his investigation.

The curious generosity of this new medical care now began to travel by grapevine up and down the desert.

CHAPTER 5

EXIT DOLLARS—ENTER GOD

So GARFIELD, feeling his way along, found by 1934 that, despite this complete care he was giving these formerly medically God-forgotten 5000 workmen, his new health plan was actually making ends meet. You protest that there must have been a colored gentleman in his economic woodpile, that our desert doctor, like Death Valley Scotty not far away, must have had some secret source of money.

Because it is a fact, notorious and scandalous, that the cost of really complete medical care is outrageous. It is bearable only by the rich. For all others (except those lucky poor who get it gratis in charity hospitals) the average doctor must be on the watch to avoid sending his sick patient from the frying pan of disease into the fire of subsequent worry about unbearable medical debt. This is medicine's tragedy: where doctors are individual businessmen dealing with the average individual sick man, they dare not sell all the science they have to offer. Their regard for the average individual's pocketbook makes it necessary for them to withhold the full power of that science.

36

They must go easy on x-rays, blood chemistry, special nursing, new chemical treatment, complicated operations —expensive procedures that, limitless, may make the difference between life and death.

All this Sidney Garfield had pondered. So long as the doctor remains a businessman who sells his services direct to the person who is sick, the doctor's commodity, good medicine, is only for the person who can buy it. But on the other hand the religion of the practice of medicine holds that the services of the physician are not only for those who can buy them but for all who need them. This is the doctor's dilemma, pointed out by Michael Davis.

Now Garfield had by-passed this tragedy—by this simple plan in which all those who are well share the burden with the sick. Our desert doctor, you understand, didn't for a moment think that this prepaid medical care plan was his own invention. He knew that such plans had long been practiced—with more or less completeness and effectiveness—by railroads like the Santa Fe and Southern Pacific, and on various western construction projects, and in certain industries in the South and East. But as his figures for his complete unlimited medical care began to change from red to black, Garfield began to detect a possibility not mentioned in any prepaid health plan he had ever heard of. The daily nickels from the workmen now more than 95 per cent signed up, and the fees from their compensation insurance care, were now doing more than pay Garfield's expenses. . . . *They were beginning to pay off the debt for that expensive little hospital.*

Now, if prepaid medicine could actually build and pay

for its facilities! If groups of doctors, scientists, and nurses could band together with groups of citizens to make medicine so profitable that it could pay for itself and build new modern hospitals! It seemed too good to be true; it seemed a silly dream. The tradition of the horse-and-buggy economics of medicine was against it.

But out there in the desert, the young dreamer, Garfield, was lucky, more lucky than original. What was original about his experiment was that he happened to be making it where there was nobody to bother him. Out here there were no medical societies, no competing doctors. Garfield's luck had in it a touch of the luck of Louis Pasteur. That old fighter was by no means the first man to dream that microbes might be man-killers. But what helped Pasteur put over his experiments was the lucky fact that he was alone, that he was not a doctor. He was only a chemist. From this wild man the organized doctors of that day felt no threat to their prevailing superstitions of the cause of infectious sickness. He was dabbling merely with the diseases of silkworms, sugar beets, or sheep. So he could prove his germ theory, not bothered by the doctors. Then when he jumped his facts from the ills of worms and sheep and mice to those of men, he could not be gainsaid, he quickly blitzed the medicos.

So now here in the desert, lonely and lucky, Garfield proved his bookkeeping of how common men can share the health. There were no medical politicians to whisper to their fellow doctors that this prepaid health plan was stealing their patients. Mind you, if there had been competing doctors there, you could hardly have blamed them for worrying about Garfield. You could not have blamed them because the vast majority of physicians did not then —and do not now—realize the contradiction faced by the doctors of the nation. It is this:

Microbe hunters, chemists, x-ray men, physiologists, internists, surgeons by thousands were making discoveries that daily were giving the practice of medicine and surgery a mightier and mightier death-fighting, health-giving power. The doctors' organizations broadcast these marvelous medical advances. They were justly proud of spearheading this vast potential lifting of the level of human life. But now came the contradiction, the confusion. This more and more mighty science cost more and more money. Group medicine giving all of the best in modern diagnosis and treatment was immensely more expensive than the laying on of hands, the prescriptions, the simple treatments and operations performed by the old-fashioned doctors. Yet in the early 1930's the rank-and-file of our physicians, though they were taught to be proud of the new medical science, were largely left with the notion that it could still be paid for, single-handed, by the individual patient, by the individual common man.

This was the failure of the leaders of the organizations of our doctors.

This was the strange confusion of these medical leaders: they were proud of scientific medical advances but at the same time seemed unaware that the life-giving power was withheld from suffering human millions. Conservative inquiry was made into the scandal of the common man's inability to pay for this new medical science. This caused hysterical indignation among certain of these medical leaders. Just before Garfield began his desert experiment, a disturbing report had been made to the country by the national *Committee on the Costs of Medical Care.* The Chairman of the committee was Dr. Ray Lyman Wilbur, past President of the American Medical Association. Nobody would call Dr. Wilbur a bolshevik. He was at this time a member of President Hoover's cabinet. And who would call Herbert Hoover a communist? But now when Dr. Wilbur's committee reported to the nation that the cost of good medical care was beyond the pocketbooks of millions, the *Journal of the American Medical Association* in an editorial said that this was "socialism and communism—inciting to revolution."

At the same time attempts of groups of citizens, banding together with physicians to organize prepaid medical care, were fought bitterly by local medical societies. There was a pattern to these far-flung battles that indicated a common strategy guided by the American Medical Association's leaders.

Now in the desert Garfield was safe from all such persecution. In the desert Garfield's health plan blossomed. He had gone heavily into debt to build his little hospital, it having cost him more than $30,000. His medical and surgical care was unlimited; only venereal disease and sickness developing before the men had come on the Aqueduct job, only these were excluded from the benefits of the nickel-a-day health plan. Sixty per cent of Garfield's total take came from the accumulation of these daily nickels. The remaining 40 per cent of it was paid him by the insurance companies for the men's industrial accident care.

In two years Garfield's debt had been paid off completely. He owned the hospital free and clear.

This gave our desert doctor courage. He built a second hospital in the hot Coachella Valley desert at the Parker Dam; and it was the delight of his keymen with the workmen's excellent medical care that first brought Garfield to the notice of Henry Kaiser. Here, too, nearly 100 per cent of the workmen joined the health plan. By this time Garfield was employing 10 well-trained physicians and surgeons, full time. In 1935, Garfield built still another, a third hospital. It likewise operated upon the same nickel-a-day health plan, at the Imperial Dam, near Yuma, Arizona.

By 1938, when all three of these desert construction projects were done, Garfield had not only paid good salaries to his physicians, nurses, technicians, and hospital staff, but he'd also paid off all equipment, owned all three hospitals, free and clear of debt, and had accumulated a reserve of $150,000. It was not his personal fortune that interested him. It was this discovery that stirred our desert doctor:

If you streamline your medical care, you can handsomely support good, complete care of relatively small groups of people, working on short time projects. You can build, you can pay off fine hospitals in a few years' time. You can do all this on an income from voluntary prepayment that is no strain upon the pocketbook of the workmen, plus a backlog of compensation insurance money that's mandatory the country over. What then could you do for the millions of America's medically neglected, on long term jobs in the nation's industrial areas?

This, finally, haunted Garfield. This streamlined medical care made everybody happy. The employers were delighted because this good medicine increased their manpower, decreased the absenteeism due to illness. The men showed their enthusiasm for the health plan by the fact that, though it was purely voluntary, they'd joined it, better than 95 per cent of 12,000 of them on three separate construction projects. That exploded the superstition that you'd get the ordinary man to think about paying for his illness only after he'd actually taken sick. The insurance companies were quick to see their bread and butter side of superior medicine in a modern hospital. The speed of recovery of their accident cases cut down the burden of their disability payments. And finally, the doctors?

Garfield's doctors were maybe happiest of all. What really stirred them was that the health plan took the money element out of their service to sick and hurt human beings. They remembered the case of a superintendent of one of the construction companies who had refused to join the nickel-a-day health plan. Later this man had come down with severe pneumonia. He had been brought to the little Desert Center Hospital, which, of course, refused nobody. There Garfield, his doctors, and nurses had tended the desperately sick superintendent, giving him the scientific works; and they pulled him through his pneumonia. Then they billed the convalescent superintendent, at regular fees—for $250. Though they had saved his life, the superintendent was now angry at the size of the bill, and refused to pay it. The doctors and nurses were sore at the superintendent. Why had he been too stupid to ante in his nickel-a-day beforehand? It was the workmen's nickels that had saved their boss's life.

Garfield treated his doctors well, paid them fairly so that they had no financial worries. He found that the better you treat your doctors, the more kindly they treat their patients. Like Garfield himself, his doctors were happiest because they could use the full power of their science. They could give all their patients unlimited hospital, medical, surgical, x-ray, laboratory, and nursing care. They did not skid on the old slimy trail of the dollar. Yet they knew that what they were giving was in no sense charity. It made them feel good to help these anonymous thousands of men who were no longer being shoved around, medically. They could shoot the works on these thousands who were miserable, sun-baked, sun-struck, under par, hurt, and sick men.

What it boiled down to for the men was that they felt they owned this health plan; they'd all helped pay for it. What it meant for the doctors was that, when there was no money consideration between them and their patients, there was the chance for simple Christianity to come in. Exit dollars—enter God.

CHAPTER 6

MEN AND KAISER—MEDICAL

EQUALS

THE SAD thing about Garfield's beautiful experiment was that it was so temporary. He had made the contractors enthusiastic by mightily raising their manpower but they were scattered now. He had brought a new kind of medical mercy to formerly medically God-forgotten dam workers, desert rats, diggers. These had been grateful but they were gone now to the four winds and who would hear their words of praise? So, for Garfield's health plan there was no chorus of hallelujah, there were no headlines in the newspapers. So now the desert doctor went back to the Los Angeles County Hospital to catch up with new discoveries in medicine and surgery—advances blossoming in bewildering profusion while he had been off in the desert proving you could bring good medicine and surgery to everybody by an easy sharing of the cost burden. Now Garfield's vision of universal medical care might easily have been buried in the desert dust. But then came Henry

Kaiser, and that chip off the old block, his son Edgar.

That most optimistic of all men, Henry Kaiser, leading his associated contractors, in 1938 was beginning to build the giant Coulee Dam on foundations begun four years before. It would turn the wild wasted water power of the Columbia River into millions of kilowatts of energy. It would transform the State of Washington's arid, desolate, rich-soiled Quincy upland into a garden spot green with orchards and gold with wheat in summer. Of millions of acres of grim land now fit only for gophers the water pumped by Coulee would make a green country for the work, the health, and happiness of millions of Americans. President Roosevelt himself visioned it as a new promised land for the Okies who were being shoved around in California. As a building project, Coulee surpassed even the ancient pyramids of Egypt. It was the most gigantic construction undertaken in all human record. It was fit peculiarly for the Paul Bunyan boldness, sweep, and energy of Henry Kaiser. Its building was to be supervised by Kaiser's son, Edgar, who had just turned 30.

The Kaisers, father and son, had this in common: that they were both deeply concerned about the health, strength, and happiness of the common as well as the uncommon men who must do this building. It is true that during the years of the digging and the laying of the foundations for this mightiest of all the works of man, before the Kaisers had come, there had been a hospital, there had been medical care. But now when he came to take over the job Edgar Kaiser discovered to his dismay that the unions—dissatisfied with this medical care—

wanted the contractors to have no part in it. The authorities of the State of Washington refused to allow Kaiser to run the hospital.

Many managers might have said, so what? These were still the 1930's, when manpower was not yet one of management's worries. Manpower was still a glut. For every worker bruised, battered, hurt, or sick, for every man worn out by work and tossed onto the human scrap pile, you could find five men to replace that used-up human being.

But it was Henry Kaiser's dream to build not only dams but men. For years the builder had been brooding over a fourth dimension of manpower. It was not only how much a man could lift, not only how quick he could think, not only how long he could work. It was the man's spirit, too, that preoccupied Henry Kaiser. It was the man's morale. And to our simple giant morale meant, simply, happiness. Kaiser was not ashamed to use that unscientific and old-fashioned word. He had puzzled it out of his experience that this intangible, this happiness, was tied up to the state of the physical functions of a man's body. He was no scientist in the narrow sense of the term, yet it was his hunch that happiness is really chemical.

About doctors Henry Kaiser had two slants. He was a fan for physicians. He knew that, in their ministrations, they were of all human beings most akin to God. But he was at the same time enraged that the godlike power of the doctors was not for all mankind equally. It was the lack of a doctor—who might have saved her life—that had killed Kaiser's own mother at the age of 49. This had burned him and he had stayed burned about it all these years. Yet, busy with his building, he hadn't found time to delve into already available co-operative prepaid medical care plans. Kaiser was not a student; he was only a builder and a dreamer. Yet to the cruelty of widespread human medical deprivation he was sensitized. He was raw about this medical injustice. It offended him that he and his family could command the best medical service, while millions of human beings were medically kicked around.

About this infamy Henry Kaiser quizzed many doctors. He was a source of affection and despair to the many physicians who knew him; and he knew a lot of them because he was their fan. Some of them denied that there was any serious injustice in the distribution of their healing art and science. None could tell him how good medicine could be made available to everybody; and Kaiser meant, literally, everybody. Though he was only a graduate of the seventh grade, Kaiser himself claimed to be something of a doctor. He even carried a little medical bag about with him. Though no chemist, he was advanced in his amateur medical science. He attributed his own vast energy in part to the new chemically pure vitamins and hormones. He believed these were new magic keys to human health and he was always giving away bottles of this chemical magic to his friends.

Now at last at Grand Coulee—by far the biggest building job he had tackled—Henry Kaiser's impatience with bad medicine for the men came to a head. The unions and the State of Washington wouldn't let him run the hospital? But he would run it. How he didn't know. He turned that little detail over to Edgar. It was a small headache to add to the epic headache of building the Coulee Dam. Henry Kaiser, genial and gentle, was a terrific father —no different to his son Edgar than to Clay Bedford or any others among his keymen.

Edgar was just the man to welcome this headache of the workmen's good medical care. He betrayed his feeling about the rights of the common man to me not long ago. That day he had taken his noon meal at the best hotel in Richmond, California, close by the Kaiser shipyards. "There were a lot of shipyard workers eating in that dining room; and you should have seen the righthand side of the menu card—prices like the Waldorf in New York," said Edgar. "The men were ordering *pheasant*. They were liking it. Believe me, they're not going to forget they once earned money enough to order pheasant," said Edgar, laughing, and in his laugh there was the ring of high approval. If a manager thinks pheasant is okay for the workmen, he is not likely to let them down on their medical care.

Now, back in 1938, at Coulee, Edgar had the same good will about the rights of the common man to good hospitals and doctors as he had today about their rights to pheasants. He went to the union leaders. When the unions grouse about doctors, you'd better listen. Like his father, Edgar knows that unions—yes, the men's *own* unions—are good, so long as they give real service in return for the dues the men pay into them. Now he told the leaders of his own experience with the medical care at Boulder Dam and Bonneville Dam projects. "It was good medical care, yes, but good for Edgar Kaiser and his family. Not so good for the workmen," said Edgar.

The union leaders listened to this youngster looking at them so directly with eyes gleaming kindly through his spectacles. He made them feel he didn't mean maybe. He made them know he made no difference between the workmen and the Kaisers. He made them see he was a straight shooter.

"Give us just one try at running the hospital and your medical care. We'll show you we can run it *right*," said Edgar.

The union leaders said okay. And so it came about that Dr. Sidney Garfield—after a very short time at brushing up on medical science at Los Angeles—found himself going north to Coulee with Mr. and Mrs. Edgar Kaiser. Edgar had heard about Garfield from H. H. Hatch and A. B. Ordway, of an industrial insurance company in which Henry Kaiser held a financial interest. They'd told Edgar that this Dr. Garfield was a wizard. That he'd taken medical care of the dam workers with a skill and at a low cost that had been wonderful for the men, good for the contractors' manpower, and profitable to the insurance companies. That was enough. Now long-distance telephoning in the Kaiser manner. And here was Garfield rushing up over the barren Washington uplands and along the mystic Grand Coulee gorge to the dam site on the Columbia River.

Garfield admitted that what he found at Coulee scared him. It was more than his old desert job of starting from scratch and building a hospital for a few thousand workers who were lucky to get any kind of medical care at all. Here at Coulee, in the deep valley of the Columbia and up the bluffs to the east and west there had mushroomed a community of more than 15,000 people. There were the Kaiser workers, many with wives and children. There was the pretty little Government City, with its model houses —but nary a doctor or hospital facility for the inhabitants, officials of the Bureau of Reclamation Service and their families. Then there were the merchants and their families. And finally, the sinister little "Hidden City." This was a rough and tumble replica of a Klondike town, housing the rag-tag-and-bobtail, male and female, to be found around giant construction projects.

During the building of the dam's foundation before the coming of Henry and Edgar Kaiser and their builders, this community had been served by half a dozen physicians. Here was what had been wrong with the medical set-up that had served the foundation men. They'd had a health plan. But the private practice of the doctors had come first. The men said it was hard to get to see the doctors. They said they were like dirt under the doctors' feet. There was an 85-bed hospital, which Garfield found to have a lot of chronic infected cases in it. The hospital had poor outpatient facilities. Men hurt—if they could walk at all—had to climb to the second floor for medical attention. The surgery was not isolated; and Garfield noticed that patients kept wandering into it—dirty in their working clothes.

"What can you do?" asked Edgar Kaiser, after Garfield had given it all the once-over. "We've asked the union

,leaders to give us a try at running the medical care. We've said we'd show them we could run it right. We can't let them down."

What Garfield recommended was drastic. The hospital would have to be built over. He'd have to get a new staff of doctors. Revamping it would take a lot of money.

"You understand," said Edgar Kaiser, who knew how brilliantly Garfield had paid off his hospitals in the desert, "you get it clear, we're not out to make money on this medical care. It would be nice if we could come out even on it. But if we have to lose money, then it's still okay."

CHAPTER 7

AMAZING—THEY STOPPED

DYING!

THERE is a simple Kaiser technique that in part explains
the so-called Kaiser miracles. Henry Kaiser began with a
hunch that workmen should have the best medical care,
that there was a way they could pay for it, and when they
got it that this would be good for their morale. He knew
nothing of the details of how to do it. He put it up to his
son, Edgar. Then Edgar promised the men he'd see they'd
have the best doctors and hospitals. He didn't know how.
So Edgar put Sidney Garfield on the spot to get them.
Garfield came to Coulee, saw that correction of the medical situation might be impossible. But there was Edgar
with the Kaiser motto. It was to the effect that the only
thing impossible is what simply can't be done. And this
could be. And Garfield could do it. So Garfield became
part of the Kaiser crew that can do anything, so long as
it is not impossible, and nothing is.

Now when Garfield took over at Coulee he showed a

curious energy. It seemed low-keyed, but it was no less fierce, no less impatient than Henry or Edgar Kaiser's, for all Garfield's subdued exterior. Now with a bold hand he wrecked the old hospital. He transformed it into a large-scale version of the beautiful little houses of healing he had built in the desert. When he put in estimates of what it would cost to air-condition the entire building—summers it could get hot at Coulee—it was pointed out to him that the finest city hospitals weren't air-conditioned!

Garfield stuck to his demand. He was for good medicine, the best medicine. When a sick man is feverish, then a hot room adds to his discomfort, and discomfort is bad medicine. Garfield let everybody know that he was first, last, and all the time for everything for the sick men. He was not a mere company doctor. Now he showed that he knew where his power lay. He had talked to the union leaders before he'd got into this argument about the cost of air-conditioning. He'd made the men air-conditioning-conscious. The hospital was air-conditioned from top to bottom.

He installed three modern operating rooms, as fine as any in the whole State of Washington. The revamping of the hospital set Kaiser and his associates back $100,000, and this seemed to be two strikes on Garfield who wanted to prove to Edgar Kaiser that he could make the medical care come out even. But this was only the beginning of the high cost of Garfield's streamlined medical care. With 5000 men, plus their wives and children to care for, Garfield saw that here was the chance to organize something beyond the prepaid medicine in good hospitals that he had given to the workmen in the desert. Here was the opportunity for group medicine practiced by a staff of specialists under one hospital roof.

Ordinary physicians and surgeons were not enough, if he was to give the Coulee people the top medical care Henry and Edgar Kaiser were demanding. You couldn't expect a general surgeon to be an expert in orthopedics to mend the smashed bones of workmen. You'd not ask an ordinary practitioner to be handling complicated childbirth or the gynecologic ills of women. You couldn't demand an unlicked cub of an intern, hardly dry behind the ears, to give children the best pediatric care. If you had a surgeon skilled in fixing the defects of human plumbing, that still left you out on the end of a limb about the diseases of the eyes, ears, nose, and throat.

When Garfield arrived to take charge at Coulee, he found the existing hospital housing some of the sad results of the practice of doctors who were specialists in nothing yet trying to be experts in everything. He found horse-and-buggy medicine caring for men building the technically most modern structure in human history.

What Garfield now went out to organize was a miniature Mayo Clinic. Nothing less would be worthy of Henry Kaiser's dream of truly good medical care, or of the modernity of what now banged, clanged, roared, rumbled, and whistled in the magic rising of the greatest dam ever conceived by man. He had a tough time assembling his needed highly trained group of specialist physicians and surgeons. He combed the State of Washington. Men with established practices wouldn't leave them to come to this temporary

Coulee job, even at the excellent salaries Garfield offered. Coulee did not have a good medical reputation. Then Garfield wired and long-distance telephoned in the Kaiser grand manner. He flew from coast to coast. Within six months he had got together his little Mayo Clinic. It was headed by an able young surgeon, Dr. Cecil Cutting, from Stanford University. It was made up of keen young men of various medical and surgical disciplines, all just out of residencies in high-grade hospitals, from California, Iowa, and as far away as Michigan. Garfield paid these doctors good salaries—$500 to $600 a month, plus their keep, plus bonuses if the project should be successful, which Garfield was sure it would be. The staff had no office rent, no other overhead to worry about. This was far beyond what any of them could have expected to earn, in their first few years out, if they had hung out their individual private practice shingles.

Immediately Garfield set up a prepaid health plan, voluntary, like his original one in the desert. It set the men back 50¢ a week off their pay checks—about 7¢ a day. The grapevine quickly spread the news of the revolution in medical care that had taken place in the now comfortable, modern Coulee hospital. When the men found that the doctors and nurses treated them as if they were every one of them as good as Edgar Kaiser, they flocked into the health plan. There was no stopping them. There is no trouble getting modestly paid men to spend the equivalent of half a pack of cigarettes a day when they know that this will guarantee them the best unlimited medical attention.

55

Quickly the men in the unions knew that Edgar Kaiser had not been kidding them. At union meetings men interrupted each other with testimonials.

"Look here," said one workman who'd been badly sick, and then cured by long expert care in the new hospital, "I've been paying 7¢ a day. But then for weeks they treated me as if I was Kaiser himself. I've figured it up. At regular doc's private practice prices this would have set me back $3000!"

But even so all was not medically lovely at Coulee. There was this plan that spread the health for the workmen. But, up till now, their wives and children must get *their* medical and hospital care at those old regular and murderous fees for service. Garfield's doctors were in a way a group of medical Dr. Jekylls and Mr. Hydes—putting the finest medicine within the reach of husbands by prepaid care, making it difficult for their wives and children by the ancient private individual fee system.

They were taking care of expectant mothers, delivering their babies, giving good science to newborn infants, curing sore throats and running ears and tending to all the contagious ills of childhood . . . at a price that takes a big chunk out of your bread and butter money if the illness is complicated or long. Now for this service to the families Sidney Garfield found that he was putting plenty of money on the books. But it was the old desert story all over: Not all of this book money was coming into the tills of the doctors. And this was not the worst of it. For, while the workmen were crazy about their personal 7¢-a-day prepaid medical care, these very men were panning the hospital, calling Garfield and his doctors gold-diggers, when the big bills came in for their care of their own wives and children.

Edgar Kaiser now came to the rescue. "Why don't we have the same kind of prepaid family plan for the wives and children?" Edgar asked Garfield.

Our desert doctor did a lot of quick figuring. Yes, they could take care of the women, he estimated, at the same price as the men—50¢ a week. After some bargaining with the union leaders, they agreed there might be an additional charge of 25¢ a week for each child brought into the family plan. The family prepaid health plan was advertised and announced at union meetings. It was an unexpected flop. Within three months' time, only some 10 per cent of the workmen's wives and children had signed up for it. What actually happened was what has defeated the bookkeeping of more than one voluntary health insurance plan. The wives and children were not signed up for it, most of them, *until they took sick.* You can see how this threatened to wreck Garfield's set-up. If only *sick* people pay 7¢ a day, any health plan would quickly run into the red. The economic success of prepaid medical care depends on the widest kind of sharing of its cost burden.

The well must help to pay for the sick, or else the sheriff will soon be at the door of the doctors.

But by now Garfield was becoming wise at putting democracy into action. He had begun to realize the immense power for good that's inherent in union organizations. He called a meeting of the union leaders. Didn't the men like the medical care they were getting? Sure.

Okay. Wonderful. Didn't their wives and children—the few who had joined the health plan—get the same good care? Of course. Fine. And look at the way it saves us money!

"Yes," said Garfield in his quiet but obstinately persuasive low-keyed way. "But the way it's going now, it's going to put the whole health plan on the rocks. How can we operate if we only get 50¢ a week from your wives *after* they're sick, and 25¢ a week from the children, the same way? It doesn't add up. The healthy ones have got to pay their share. Or we'll have to close down the family plan."

This was real labor-management co-operation. Once the union leaders saw the justice of it, they went to town with the union members. And within a month, 90 per cent of the families had flocked into the prepaid health plan.

This left only the Government people—for whom the Government had supplied no doctors or hospitals—and the merchants and their families—and the people of the Hidden City. For these the health plan was not opened. But at Coulee there were no other doctors than Garfield's. With their income from the private practice upon the workmen's families now almost completely cut off, you'd have expected that there would be a drop in the private income of the Coulee Hospital. This is the bogey that has long frightened physicians in private practice. They fear that prepaid medical care plans in their communities will take away their privately paying customers. But now the expected drop in the hospital's private income did not happen.

What could this mean? Only that Garfield, at last getting the men's families into the health plan, had un-covered a section of the population that had been up till then medically neglected. The women knew that they and their children would have to pay big prices for the good medical care they'd get, at private practice rates, at the Coulee Hospital. So, for what they thought to be ordinary illnesses, for early stages of sickness, fearing these charges, they stayed at home hoping they'd get away with it, hoping they'd get better without medical care at all. They'd wait to go to the doctor and the hospital till they were good and sick. Maybe desperately sick. This is the opposite of preventive medicine, for it is fundamental that illness is most curable in its beginning.

Garfield was delighted by the result of this unintended experiment. "We can tell the doctors of this country," he said, "that the people they're going to serve on prepaid health plans are people who in general are not getting early and proper medical care at the present time."

But here was a still more unexpected result of taking the workmen's families into the health plan. The private practice income of the hospital and the doctors, not only did not go down, but it went up by 10 per cent in the two years that followed. For this, too, Garfield saw the simple explanation. The people from Government City and the merchant's city were stirred to come in greater numbers for medical care at regular fees—by the excel-lence of the group medical care and the hospital accommo-dations, made possible by the prepaid health plan financed by the half-dollars of the workmen and their families.

This little model of a Mayo Clinic had made the entire

Coulee community conscious of the value of early medical care in a way they'd never been before. There was no question that people who could pay at private fees, would pay—provided the medicine they got was good.

Not long ago Dr. Garfield was called to testify on Kaiser's Coulee health plan at a Senate hearing on today's lack of medical care suffered by civilian America because of the deprivation of doctors during wartime. "The most amazing part of the whole thing," said Garfield, "was that when we had the plan started and well along in operation, people stopped dying.

"That sounds funny, but actually what it meant was that people came to us; the reason they stopped dying was the fact that they came to us with their early symptoms. *There wasn't the factor of medical cost to keep them away.*" Garfield underlined that, accenting it with all the fire of faith that smoldered under his outward shyness.

"They could come to us with the first pain in their abdomen, when they first caught their colds, and we would catch their appendicitis cases before they ruptured, and would get their pneumonia cases before they were terminal, and we would take care of them and get them well," he said.

CHAPTER 8

COURAGE AT GRAND

COULEE

TELLING his story of those lives saved by modern medicine at Grand Coulee, Garfield—not intending it—made me see the reverse side of that happy picture, in far-flung regions of our country where this prepaid group medical care is not yet available. I could visualize a procession of coffins. Large and small they daily leave workmen's houses and the homes of middle-bracket Americans. Here men and women may have been too proud to ask for medical charity. They may have hesitated to declare themselves "medically indigent." They may have felt it best to save the money that might have bought the early, scientific, medical care that could have kept them or their children from dying. There is no census of these people lost because they feel themselves too poor to go to the doctor early. There are no statistics counting Americans not too poor to eat, shelter, or clothe themselves, yet still too poor to save themselves from death.

At the Senate hearing where Dr. Garfield told his Coulee story, his testimony was confirmed by Henry Kaiser. To the listeners the contrast between the bold builder and his soft-spoken medical chief must have been astounding. Yet there was no question that in the matter of the technical details of Coulee's prepaid health plan, Garfield had been Kaiser's teacher. But now in Kaiser's own testimony you could feel that big builder groping toward a vast nationwide expansion of medical care, peering toward health horizons which Garfield had not yet imagined. Kaiser saw that Garfield had the local know-how. Kaiser realized the condition of millions of Americans who today must stay away from the doctor unless very sick; or must accept the indignity of charity; or must be treated at cut-rates unjust to the physicians; or must worry under the burden of unbearable debt. . . . One third of the loans by certain of the large personal loan companies —with their murderous interest rates—are made for the paying off of their doctor and hospital bills.

Kaiser had firm hold of these grim fundamentals. He had long believed what Garfield had now demonstrated at Coulee: that the majority of people want to pay for their medical care. Furthermore, Kaiser had not lost faith in the doctors, so increasingly powerful in their life-saving science yet so curiously antiquated in the economics of its possible spread to everybody. He believed they were the most valuable of our citizens, and that they should be well paid for their service. Now here at Coulee, at least, Garfield had proved that good doctors, and especially young doctors, do not insist on being individual businessmen.

They do not mind working on salaries if these are good, and if they have the chance to use the marvelous power of modern medical science—unhampered by the dead hand of no dollars.

But at Coulee Garfield had taught Henry Kaiser another fundamental. Neither Henry Kaiser, nor his son Edgar, had expected this one. Edgar had told Garfield, you recall, that it would be nice if they could come out even, but that if they had to lose money for the workers' medical and hospital care, then it would still be okay. But here now was the astounding result of the Coulee health plan. All the money for the rebuilding of the hospital, installing the expensive x-ray and laboratories, hiring the high-priced staff of doctors and surgeons— within three years all that had been *paid off* in full, lock, stock, and barrel. Now Kaiser saw new medical horizons. Here was what industry, the doctors, communities could do. When they banded together to prepay their medical care. When their health plan was well managed. When the medicine is streamlined. When it is made economical as well as effective by grouping teams of doctors, handy to laboratories, x-ray, and to each other all under one hospital roof.

But this was mere bookkeeping; and on his trips to the Coulee Dam, while it was building, Henry Kaiser had made what was for him a deeper observation. Never before had he seen such energy, such enthusiasm in any of his working armies. Accustomed as he was to fast construction, Kaiser was astounded at the tempo of the rising of the mass of Coulee. Now he believed he had found the reason. For years he had been groping for that fourth dimension of manpower—"happiness." Now he saw this happiness in action, this morale which—in the poetry of Pare Lorentz—drives men, brawny, "to move mountains and shove rivers around."

To his discovery of this secret of the fourth dimension of manpower Henry Kaiser testified. He was asked the following question by Senator Claude Pepper . . .

"You found . . . that when you installed these medical facilities, you were not only able to stop deaths of a great many of your employees by medical attention brought to them before their illness became acute, but immediately absenteeism from illness diminished, and you got a greater working efficiency out of your employees?"

"That is absolutely true," answered Henry Kaiser.

He knew that the health of the men, and their happiness at the health of their families, had both been powerful factors in the finishing of the Coulee Dam a year and a half ahead of schedule. But the big builder does not fancy the word "efficiency" applied to human beings. He reserves it for the working of machines.

"And we got something beyond mere efficiency," Kaiser told the senators. "We got greater confidence, also, out of our employees, and faith, and more courage."

CHAPTER 9

THE GIANT SEEMS
FORGETFUL

IF WE free their hands, if we let them use all their science, our doctors can do more than merely mend bone and brain and muscle. They can build faith and courage in the common man. This was the fact that Kaiser saw at Coulee. For seeing it he will be remembered long after the giant generators and pumps of Coulee have turned to rust, long after the mighty concrete mass of the dam itself has begun to crumble. For understanding that simple fact, and wanting to take action upon it, Kaiser—not a doctor—ranks with the great physicians. Action upon that simple fact would begin to put medicine where it truly belongs: founded upon science, yet above and beyond mere science in its aim and spirit. To Kaiser—only a contractor—this fact promised a blueprint for human brotherhood for to-morrow. But now in 1940 Henry Kaiser had to pigeon-hole this discovery. In that sinister year all dreams of truth, health, and happiness were a dime a dozen. All possibility of human progress was in mortal jeopardy from the upsurge of the haters of humanity, the liars, killers, and destroyers.

Long before Kaiser, the death-fighter Louis Pasteur had sensed the looming of today's calamity of worldwide war. In his prime Pasteur had been, like Kaiser, optimistic. He had foretold the glorious possibility of ridding mankind of all microbic maladies. Later in his wise and gloomy older age Pasteur had given his disciples this warning:

"Two opposing laws seem to me now in contest," he said. "The one, a law of blood and death. The other, a law of peace, work, health. . . . Which of these laws will prevail, God alone knows."

Now in 1940 Pasteur's predicted Armageddon was in full tide of battle; and it seemed that the law of blood and death bid fair to triumph. Among Americans, while millions still thought themselves safe from the destroyers, Henry Kaiser was among the first to see what was at stake not only for America but for mankind. Like Pasteur, his religion was work, health, and peace. But Kaiser's common sense told him that the threat of blood and death could only be fought by a new super-production, by giant building of a speed and vastness impossible by all present rules of human engineering. This was why this hopeful experiment in good medicine for the common man was forgotten for a moment. That was why Kaiser's discovery that good medicine means human faith and courage became submerged for him. To fight the threat of blood and death Kaiser now began to plan and put into operation new and strange and terrific projects of construction.

These he began on a scale unprecedented in American history, long before America was forced to join the world-wide battle.

As a sand-and-gravel man during the building of the dams at Boulder, Bonneville, and Coulee, Henry Kaiser had begun to earn a still purely Western fame for phenomenal construction. This did not rest upon his enforcing of a human speed-up, or the sinister stretch-out, or any driving of workers beyond the limits of human endurance. Kaiser's work had never been interrupted by a strike. Nor was it to be explained by any new genius for super-mechanization, though, mind you, Kaiser never thought men should do what machines could perform easier, faster, better. But what you noted about Kaiser's record-breaking construction, as you watched it at Coulee, was this especially: that none of the thousands of workers hurried, that all of them seemed to be taking it strangely easy at their so-called toil. Instead of being the slaves of their great machines, you felt, watching the humblest workers, that they were the masters of the hysters, the whirlies, and the giant hammer-head cranes that carried the concrete and steel to them.

Henry Kaiser explained it not by any jargon to be found in engineering science. He described it in strange words of poetry and music. The secret of this building, so effortless, so seeming lazy, so speedy, said Kaiser, lay in "getting the right rhythm of flow of materials and men."

So now at the beginning of the 1940's, west of the Rockies, if you covered the water front and cocked your ear, you could hear the mighty opening chords of an ultra-modern, exultant music. It was defiant and optimistic. It was the opposite of decadent. It was foreboding for the degenerate destroyers, the enemies of mankind. Such were the banging, clanging, whistling, roaring, shouting symphonies of a new fantastic construction. They had the defiance of Beethoven's 5th Symphony, the torrential energy of the Scherzo of his 9th. The instruments that made this new music were labor-saving hysters, hammer-head cranes and whirlies. The musicians were scores of thousands of steel-helmeted men, who took it so curiously easy at their working. The concert-masters were the Kaiser keymen. The composer and conductor was Henry Kaiser.

At Permanente, California—seemingly out of nothing—there arose a giant new industry. In one year it turned out all the cement for the Shasta Dam. Then it became vital in the desperate emergency of the re-building of Pearl Harbor.

Steel was wanting in the West. Now on a pig ranch among the pleasant orchards at Fontana, California, within one year there grew out of nothing the first steel plant west of the Rockies, complete from blast furnace to rolling mills.

Steel-making demands coal and iron: simultaneously these began to pour out of the earth at new Kaiser mines at Sunnyside, Utah, and Kelso, California.

Light metals would soon be in desperate demand for aircraft; and soon magnesium began to hiss and sputter out of a new chemical plant at Permanente.

At Richmond, California, and Portland, Oregon, Kaiser's rhythm of flow of materials and men began to build Liberty boats in days where before they were made in months.

At Vancouver, Washington—against the naval lore and science of our eminent admirals—Kaiser's project for swarms of aircraft carriers began to take shape in a fashion ominous for Hirohito.

Liberty ships might not be enough to keep the life-lines open for the far-flung armies of the United Nations. Though denied airplane metals, now at Los Angeles Henry Kaiser—along with Howard Hughes—began planning fleets of thousands of plywood cargo airplanes, boxcars in the sky.

Kaiser's keymen, his two sons, Edgar and Henry Jr., included, were driven to the limit of their strength, and then beyond it, yet kept on working. Henry Kaiser himself enjoyed it. To super-charge his natural super-energy the giant demanded more and better vitamins. New pills of these powerful chemicals were recommended to him, but with the warning that they might rob him of sleep if he took too many.

"That's just what I want," roared Kaiser. "How many of these pills will I have to take to sleep less, or maybe even not at all?" he asked, laughing.

So it came about that this unprecedented industrial mobilization of a vast new working army in the West by Henry Kaiser had contradictory consequences. In the first place it caused him to forget that Garfield's prepaid group medical care could build faith and courage in the common man. But in the second place this same expansion brought about a mighty migration of workers to the West; and now by 1942 Henry Kaiser woke up to find that he had no medical corps to build faith and courage in his industrial army.

Meanwhile by the end of 1940, Sidney Garfield had faded from active participation in this boisterous booming industrial music. His work there completed, the red-headed doctor had left Coulee. Back once more he had gone to Los Angeles, to his old surgical chief at the Los Angeles County Hospital, to brush up on new surgical science. He was an officer of the Medical Reserve Corps of the army, and expected to be called to war. The first pilings for the Kaiser-Richmond shipyards were driven in January, 1941. By June that year, 16,000 men were already shouting, swearing, getting hurt, and fumbling at Kaiser's fantastic new technique of Liberty ship construction. In those months the population of Richmond, California, had nearly doubled, to beyond 30,000. There began to be muttering among the men about long waits in the local doctors' offices.

Now it was lucky for the workers—and for prepaid group medicine—that there were two chips off the old block, Henry Kaiser. Henry Kaiser Jr. was only 24. He was handling all personnel and labor relations problems at the new shipyards. Like his older brother, Edgar, this youngster knew that a most powerful bond in the always uneasy relationship between a man and his manager is the action of a manager in the matter of the total condition of the man's body. To both Edgar and Henry Jr. that meant wages and housing, but more, it meant health. So Henry Jr. telephoned to Garfield, enthusiastic to have him come up to organize a medical care and hospital service at the shipyards, comparable to that of Coulee.

Garfield came up, was quietly happy at Henry Jr.'s enthusiasm, but took it easy. In the California desert and at Coulee there had been no medical competition, no medical societies, no other doctors. Garfield knew that the divine art of healing, though it is threatening to become a science, is still a business. He knew that doctors are sensitive, not only to new individual doctors coming into their communities, but especially to the threat of groups of doctors coming to make mass medicine on a prepaid health plan.

Henry Jr. wouldn't let Garfield worry about it. Together they checked up on the Richmond medical and hospital situation and found it already to be definitely inadequate. The hospitals were full to the brim; the physicians admitted they couldn't handle the new medical burden. With Henry Jr. pressing for it, Garfield worked up a prospectus and plan for an ideal hospital set-up for the yards. To the industrial insurance companies, handling the workmen's compensation insurance, the two of them explained how vital their co-operation would be. Alas, these were new insurance companies not experienced with the Coulee set-up, and to Henry Jr.'s bitter disappointment the plan fell through.

Garfield went back to Los Angeles. Months drifted by. But then came Pearl Harbor. The U. S. Maritime Commission demanded the impossible, asked limitless Liberty boats from Henry Kaiser; and within a month the Richmond shipbuilding army doubled to 30,000 workers. Now medical hell broke loose; and Clay Bedford, the Kaiser keyman managing the Richmond yards, began to be bothered by a drop in the men's morale. This was the chance for Henry Jr. Now events argued for him with power beyond that of any words. Men taking sick, who last month might have had to wait hours in the local doctors' offices, now were lucky if they could get to see a physician at all.

Now Henry Jr. really went into action. He is a young man with a pleasant face, open like a custard pie and with no guile behind it. He first sold the insurance companies whose lack of co-operation had scuttled his original effort. Now it was easier because those companies were in danger of running into the red because of the miserable medical handling of the hurt workmen. Then he went to the workmen. They looked at his eyes, beaming behind their spectacles. They saw he was no double-talker. They felt that— like his brother Edgar—he was a straight-shooter as he painted them a picture of the new kind of scientific medical and hospital care they could get for only 50¢ a week deducted from their wages.

Skillfully Henry Jr. now used the old Kaiser leadermen who'd experienced Garfield's medical mercy at Coulee. They were muttering and griping now and asking why the hell they couldn't have what they'd got up at the Dam. Now Henry Jr. enlisted them as his assistants to convert the union leaders. He was powerfully backed by Clay Bedford. So it came about that Henry Jr. and the workmen together reminded Henry Kaiser.

CHAPTER 10

DOCTORS GO WHERE FOLKS
HAVE DOUGH

So THEN came Pearl Harbor; and now Henry Kaiser, thanks to his 24-year-old son, swung into medical action, picked up the thread of his discovery that scientific medicine can build faith and courage in the common man. Again Garfield was summoned by long-distance telephone by Henry Jr. from his Los Angeles obscurity, asked to map out a health plan for 30,000 medically imperiled workers: there was no time to lose. The desert doctor located a dilapidated old building that had once housed Fabiola Hospital, in Oakland, 12 miles from the new Richmond shipyards. He calculated it would take $250,000 to rebuild it so that it would be good enough for Kaiser workers; that was the tough part of dealing with Kaiser: for his men nothing could be medically too good. Garfield expertly estimated operating costs of the proposed hospital staffed with a group of highly trained doctors, technicians, nurses.

Kaiser had only one hour's time for a conference with

Garfield on the yellow streamliner between Oakland and Sacramento on which the big builder was rushing East.

"How much will it cost to take the best medical care of 30,000 men?" asked Kaiser.

"It really won't cost anything," answered Garfield.

Then he explained that the whole project would pay itself off reasonably quickly, from the money rolling in from the weekly 50¢ pieces voluntarily prepaid by 30,000 workers, plus fees from their industrial compensation insurance.

"It won't cost *anything?*" asked Kaiser, beaming. "All right then, doctor. *You* build it. You'll be able to get money at the bank if the bankers know it really won't cost anything."

This was needling, characteristic of the giant. Garfield left the streamliner at Sacramento with this tremendous project for the hospital, the health care of 30,000 people, all in his own lap. It dazed him. Could he be sure of his revolutionary new medical bookkeeping? Clay Bedford, Kaiser's Richmond shipyard keyman, took Garfield to the bankers. Dead-pan they looked over his proposal. Could you blame them? Who'd ever regarded a hospital as a sound investment? How many hospitals were anything but financial pains-in-the-neck? Who'd ever heard of the earnings of a hospital quickly amortizing its construction? The bankers would have to study the whole thing over before they could give Garfield their answer. Before they answered, Kaiser had Garfield on the long-distance from Washington.

"Hold everything. Don't move till I get back. I'll take

it over. I'll find the money for your hospital," said Kaiser. Now he was deep into it. He told Garfield he'd gone to work on the War Department, that he'd got Lt. Sidney R. Garfield released from his hospital unit, about to be mobilized. Released—for medical care of shipyard workers! Amazing. . . . "You say you can pay this hospital off. Then, after that, how're we going to run it so there'll be no profits?" asked Kaiser. And he meant no profits.

By the time Kaiser had returned West, Garfield was ready with a smart idea, really a wonderful idea, put into his head by his medical friend, Dr. Ray Kay. "You and Mrs. Kaiser can make it a Foundation," Garfield said. "A Foundation not for profit. Then when our health plan has paid this one off, with all the money coming in we can do great scientific things, we can build *new* hospitals, more hospitals. . . ."

What began as a proposed 10-minute interview turned into an all-day conference, with Henry Kaiser—a terrific man for details—plugging up every loophole, making sure that this Foundation would serve the workmen, serve the public. So the Permanente Foundation was founded by Henry and his wife Bess Kaiser. This young Dr. Garfield might have all the figures to prove this was a wonderful investment, but the bankers were very pleased with Henry Kaiser's signature on the $250,000 loan. What if the war would end quickly? What if this shipbuilding would blow up? Then Henry Kaiser—already in hock to the hilt for his far-flung enterprises—the builder would then be holding the bag, not they, the bankers. This was okay with Kaiser.

Doctors Go Where Folks Have Dough

Now in April, 1942, armed with priorities, Garfield began buying the very finest medical, surgical, x-ray, and laboratory equipment; began tearing the insides out of the old Fabiola Hospital; began looking round for top-flight surgeons and physicians; began an adventure full of danger, to Garfield himself, and to Henry Kaiser.

Up till now they had been doing their health plan pioneering at Coulee where there was no medical competition. It had been a health plan Klondike with only Garfield there to pan the gold. But now here he was daring a spectacular adventure in the heavily populated region of San Francisco Bay, where many doctors with their powerful medical societies had been long established. Already his unorthodox, some said crazy, shipbuilding was putting a national spotlight upon Kaiser. Now, at these same shipyards, besides building the top parts of Liberty boats upsidedown, here Kaiser proposed to let his workers buy the best medical science, for next to nothing. Yet at the same time he was paying those workers terrific wages that made all good capitalists moan with anguish. If there was so much money coming into the Bay region, why shouldn't the local doctors have their share? Why would *they* go to the doctors Garfield must import for his health plan? So what? So now blithely, as he took on any fight for his key-men, Henry Kaiser plunged Garfield into the medical battle of the century.

For this, nationwide, was now at issue: Who has the right to determine how the doctor shall be paid? Is this the right of the sick people? Or will the way to pay be dictated by the doctors?

Doctors Go Where Folks Have Dough

The American Medical Association upheld that this was the right of the doctors, as organized into the Association's constituent County and State Medical Societies. These bodies—local, state, and national—represented physicians "who, in truth, desired that they and all others should practice independently on a fee-for-service basis . . . where whatever arrangement for payment each doctor had was a matter that lay between him and his patient in each individual case of service or treatment." *

Now this was the precise opposite of what was intended by Henry Kaiser and Sidney Garfield. The new Permanente Foundation intended that groups of doctors, paid by salary, should practice their healing art and science upon as many thousands of men and women as Kaiser might need to hire to build the ships to win the war. The arrangement of payment was for all these men and women to pay their weekly four bits into a common pool: not a sou marquee would pass between them and their doctors.

So here around San Francisco Bay it seemed that a battle must be joined between the new medical economics and the old.

Wasn't Kaiser getting ready to tackle a Tartar? Gaily and boldly he had launched into cement plants that were unnecessary, magnesium factories that were impossible, steel mills that were foolish, prefabricated boats that were fantastic. But here now, starting out to be a mass-doctor with his new health plan, Kaiser was challenging a vested interest that was most ancient. When you're sick and desperately need your doctor and he helps to save your life,

* Unanimous opinion, Supreme Court of the United States, January, 1943.

77

he is akin to God. You do not question his skill with his knives and serums; you should not question his bookkeeping. It may be a bit horse-and-buggy, compared to his science which is modern and marvelous. But aren't doctors above all professional men the darlings of the people? Shouldn't they be above all men—privileged? Kaiser had better be careful about how he tried to introduce his newfangled notions into doctoring!

This immunity of doctors from really effective mass indignation was undoubted. And, during the past 20 years, their remarkable advances—for which we must thank the doctors—made medicine too costly for the common man. So it was inevitable, since the individual sick man must pay his doctor, that doctors will go where sick folks have the dough. This had brought about a mal-distribution of medical care that stank to high heaven.

This was the reason for the high concentration of physicians, and most of the best physicians, who deserve the most money, on practices among Park Avenue people, among Gold Coast folks of our cities in general. This lay behind the high concentration of good doctors in cities and their sparseness in rural regions where farmers simply do not have the dough. This accounted for the notorious lack of specially trained physicians in vast regions of our nation—only 10 certified eye specialists in the whole State of Georgia, for example, only 16 in Nebraska, only 18 in Kentucky—and in each of those States all but two of these were concentrated in two big cities.

Under any system, if a doctor is a good one, he's bound to go where he can make a good living. Under the present system of individual fees-for-service, doctors go where folks have dough. Now for the past 15 years and more, groups of citizens, unable to afford the best medical care, had tried to take this matter into their own hands, had tried to correct this unjust and cruel situation. They had organized medical co-operatives. To serve these they had hired salaried groups of doctors. For the doctors who joined them this was an awful ethical transgression. In California, Arkansas, Oklahoma, Wisconsin, these brave little enterprises had been roughly handled by the American Medical Association and its constituent State and County Medical Societies. So roughly, indeed, that it was at the risk of his economic neck that any doctor took a job with such co-operatives.

So the spread of these groups had remained feeble. Their number had remained small in proportion to the millions of our medical have-nots. And for a reason. From Chicago, headquarters of the American Medical Association, down through every State and County Medical Society from coast to coast, there reached an invisible but powerful hand. This hand was ready to give the works to any physician, a member of the Medical Association in good standing, who'd go off the reservation by daring to serve a medical co-operative on a full-time salary.

How then, faced with the necessity of the medical care of 30,000 workers where the medical societies were powerful, would Garfield recruit a staff of good surgeons and physicians?

CHAPTER 11

KAISER DOESN'T BELIEVE
IN FAILURE

FOR GARFIELD the job of getting good doctors for the new Kaiser health plan was likely to be a tough one. Not only was our vastly expanding Army hungry for young and highly trained physicians. But right now, in 1942, good doctors might well shy off from salaried work for prepaid health plans, because their right to do this was still in grave legal contest in Washington, D. C. Till that savage battle was settled you could hardly blame any doctor for not joining an enterprise that might ruin his medical life.

Certain government employees in Washington had organized a non-profit organization, the Group Health Association. Physicians were employed on full-time salaries to give the members medical and hospital care on a risk-sharing prepayment basis. What now immediately happened to the doctors and the patients of Group Health was really something, in our supposedly free America. The attack was spear-headed by the District of Columbia Medical Society. It was backed by the formidable power of the American Medical Association.

To understand this truly historic battle it is necessary to know the aims and purposes of this powerful and in almost every sense magnificent association of doctors. Thanks to the A.M.A., the education of our physicians has been vastly lifted in its standards; the deadly old commercial medical colleges—diploma mills—are gone with the dodo. The American Medical Association has fought for the high training and set the high standards that make our doctors, scientifically, the best in the world. It has vigorously attacked quackery outside its own ranks. It has made hospitals far safer places for the sick man to go. Its official *Journal* is generally on the alert to report the soundest and the most up-to-date scientific information to all the doctors of the Association. So it has been an immense force for good for medical science.

But at the same time the American Medical Association has fought to defend the antiquated tradition that the individual sick man must pay his individual doctor. To defend this ancient medical right, it was clear to the strategists of the A.M.A.'s high command that it would be dangerous to permit the success of a medical co-operative right under the noses of our lawmakers and the radicals of the New Deal. So this new Group Health project had no sooner got going than the American Medical Association and its local society turned the heat upon the luckless Group Health doctors.

For their "ethical" crime of working on salaries for

groups of people prepaying their medical care, these physicians were threatened with expulsion from the A.M.A. One of the doctors was expelled. Group Health physicians were denied their vital contact with Washington specialists, one of whom was also threatened with expulsion for merely consulting with a Group Health doctor.

There are grim penalties accompanying this medical blacklist. The doctor ejected from the American Medical Association finds that he cannot get malpractice insurance, and so cannot defend himself against ambulance-chasing lawyers. He finds it hard to hire assistants. He cannot take patients to hospitals for fear (by hospital authorities) that they will lose the good rating of their hospitals—which rating is controlled by the A.M.A. And if, thus outcast, the physician tries to move to another state, there is danger that there he will be denied a license to practice his profession. On every American doctor there is a dossier at the Association's G.H.Q. in Chicago.

In organized medicine's attack upon Group Health, the group's patients suffered, along with their harassed physicians. In certain Washington hospitals these doctors were not allowed to attend their Group Health patients—even when their illness was an emergency. One patient, so a Group Health official testified, had been given a morphine injection just preparatory to the removal of his appendix; all was ready for the operation whereupon the hospital suddenly refused use of its facilities—and ordered removal of the patient.

Now it is a quality of Americans—may it never die—that they will stand being shoved around just so much and just so long. So it came about that the District of Columbia Medical Society and the American Medical Association and 21 physicians—officials of these bodies—were indicted in 1938 by the U. S. Department of Justice under the Sherman anti-trust law. Divested of its legal jargon the issue boiled down to this—

Shall the people have a say in how to pay their doctors? Or shall organized medicine dictate how physicians shall be paid? Or else, no doctor—even if you're going to die?

Here was what looked like an Armageddon, a knock-down-and-drag-out fight to a finish between the old medical economics and the new. It was a test case for the nation. In its indictment the Department of Justice charged that "the illegal activities of organized medicine in this instance are typical of what has occurred in other cities throughout the country whenever co-operative health groups have been formed."

During three years a strange war of words raged in the courts in Washington. During all this time the high-powered attorneys for the A.M.A. kept the case batting back and forth from low courts to higher, in a pea-soup fog of legal verbiage and obfuscation. The Medical Association had been indicted for "restraint of trade." The idea! Medicine is not a trade. It is a profession. This legal double-talk actually threw the case out of the lower court in the opening skirmishes of the battle. Yet through all the fog of words it still could be seen that the persecution of Group Health had been flagrant. So the District Medical Society and the A.M.A. were convicted of conspiracy to keep citizens from grouping to hire their doctors in such a way that all, well and sick, could share the risks of illness. This conviction was upheld by the Circuit Court of Appeals.

Even then the issue remained in confusion before the American people and the nation's physicians. The Medical Society and Association were found guilty of thus conspiring. But the 21 physicians, responsible officials of these same organizations, were acquitted or found not guilty of conspiracy. Who then actually engineered this persecution of Group Health? Who were the actual conspirators, the culprits? Surely not the entire American Medical Association. That great national body, more than 100,000 strong, is made up of a vast majority of doctors who are men of good will, not politicians, finaglers, or conspirators. They are physicians and surgeons doing the best medical job they can. They are neither mossback nor progressive. Many of them are vaguely disturbed that all is not well with the way millions of people have to pay for their medical care.

In the American Medical Association there are powerful constituent bodies, like the California Medical Association and the Michigan State Medical Society, that are actually fighting to bring about prepaid medicine. In any County Medical Society you're likely to find doctors ashamed of their own powerlessness to bring good medicine to all who are in need of it. In all the vast organization of our physicians you find a rank and file who practice the best medicine they know how and concern themselves hardly at all with medical politics. You find an *élite* of men of medical technique and science far too busy to bother whether Dr. Doakes or Surgeon Spelvin is elected to the House of Delegates—the governing body of the A.M.A.

So with the doctors it is the same as it is with the plumber's union or the undertaker's trade association or the Orthodox Russo-Greek Church in the days of Leo Tolstoy. That immortal defined the church simply, as "power in the hands of certain men." So with the national organization of our physicians. It is run by a few men in the little smoke-filled room. Of this fact the medical rank and file are not aware or to it they are indifferent. With this fact many of our most competent doctors are disgusted.

Now in the celebrated case at law in Washington the men behind the medical scene had not been convicted. And now, 1942, while Garfield was trying to find physicians for his health plan, the final decision regarding guilt or innocence of the American Medical Association had not been voiced by the Supreme Court of the United States. Here lay Garfield's danger. The California Medical Association is the most progressive in the country. Yet even it had constituent medical societies hard-boiled against prepaid medical care. Now if the Supreme Court failed to confirm the conviction, if the American Medical Association was adjudged *not* guilty, then health planners beware!

This was what haunted Garfield: the invisible hand from Chicago.

Until this issue was decided, who could blame physicians for being cagey about signing up with Kaiser's health plan, despite the superb facilities Garfield was installing in the new Permanente Hospital, despite the excellent salaries he was offering? This was Garfield's peril. He had promised Henry Kaiser a model of a Mayo Clinic for the common man. He had said that this would raise Kaiser's manpower. He had said the health plan could pay off this beautiful Permanente Hospital now rising out of the dirt and debris of the old Fabiola. All this now lay in jeopardy. For modern medicine is not mere bricks and mortar, steel and concrete. It is not only costly operating tables, sterilizers, x-ray apparatus, and laboratories. Modern medicine will be exactly as good as the men you get to man it. Detecting the illnesses of these new thousands of shipyard workers in the early stages, treating them speedily, curing them expertly, sending them quickly back into ship-production—all this could not be done, Garfield knew, with just any old doctors. It meant exquisite teamwork of general surgeons, orthopedists, urologists, ear-nose-throat men, internists, physiotherapists—along with x-ray men and laboratorians.

In short it meant modern group medicine of the type you find at clinics like the Lahey, the Crile, or the Mayo. How, with good conscience, could Sidney Garfield ask the highly specially trained young men that he needed to join an enterprise in which they stood a chance to become medically outcast? It is precisely the best young physicians and surgeons who—having the most to lose—do not want to become medical pariahs. Yet, if Garfield manned his Permanente Hospital with medical stumble-bums—always available a dime a dozen—his health plan was sure to fail. The hospital would jam up with sick people who would not get well. The workmen would reject the health plan. Its income would dwindle. Kaiser would be left with that $250,000 note to which he had signed his name. And Garfield? He would be ruined.

This was what now loomed over him. The technique by which co-operative medical enterprises can be sabotaged is as simple as it is effective. Good doctors are threatened away from them by the danger of the blacklist. Then the enterprise is forced to hire doctors not so good. Then the subscribers do not get the medical and surgical care they've been promised. Then the membership dwindles. Then the spokesmen for the medical societies can say, regretfully, Yes, prepaid group medicine is a wonderful idea. But it isn't practical. You see, the trouble is that good physicians do not like to join it. Isn't it too bad they don't get better doctors?

Yet now in spite of these sinister possibilities, Sidney Garfield began hiring highly trained young surgeons and physicians. He was quiet, but he was strangely persuasive. And then, too, there was this to aid him: among youngsters just out of their hospital residencies there was a new spirit of medical unrest. They were medically democratic. They believed that the best medicine should be for everybody. They knew that group medicine today is the only good medicine. Many of them had no ambition to become rich specialists, super-medical-businessmen. Many in their hospital lives had tasted the thrill of giving the godlike power of science to the poorest man or woman or child.

So Garfield began to hire his staff. After all, he *had* to hire them. Because when you promise Kaiser, you deliver.

That's one of his secrets as the teacher, the builder of his remarkable keymen who do the impossible whether they operate in ships, cement, steel, magnesium, dams—or medicine. His friend, Dr. Ray Lyman Wilbur, puts it in a nutshell.

"You see," says Dr. Wilbur drily, "Henry Kaiser does not believe in failure."

All well and good, but still, if the Supreme Court did not confirm the American Medical Association's guilt of conspiring against prepaid group medicine, then there was an excellent chance that the invisible hand would reach west from its A.M.A. headquarters in Chicago. Kaiser was already too much of a national hero to be allowed to stage a spectacular success in co-operative medicine. That invisible hand might keep Garfield out of membership in the Alameda County Medical Society, or jerk him out if he'd already been allowed to join. Even if Garfield's service to Kaiser shipyard workers was saving their lives, raising their manpower, even then there would very likely begin a subtle undermining of his medical standing. That was a technique by which the archimandrites of medicine, the "certain men in power," maintained their undemocratic medical *status quo*. All these disasters might well happen.

If it were not for Henry Kaiser himself. For, though he does put his keymen on the spot to do the impossible, even if he does not believe they should fail, he also helps them not to. Let them become entangled, during their building, in a situation where the elements are implacably against them, or human enemies are trying to smear them, then Kaiser is like a strong and gentle father.

Henry Kaiser was not aware of the foreboding medical danger to Garfield, except in a general way. Of course he did know of the strange human resistance to all change, the savage human hatred of all true pioneering. But Kaiser had no acquaintance among the high politicians of organized medicine. Yet he had close friends among good physicians and surgeons whose strength lies not in political conniving but in their superb medical and surgical competence.

These friends knew that good medicine for everybody was Kaiser's religion.

If and when the invisible hand should reach out for Garfield, Kaiser believed that these medical friends would stand up and be counted. They would be on the side of truth, justice, and human life.

CHAPTER 12

LUCKY THERE WAS PEARL HARBOR

"Disaster? Why, we progress because of disaster."

This grim, cheerful motto is at the heart of Kaiser's rule of life. It helps explain his optimism, so indomitable. It helps uncover the why of his lack of fear of mankind's seemingly so dismal future, his unconcern about his own perpetually dangerous tomorrow. For in his building he is a gambler in the grand manner. Just after the oil tanker *Schenectady* broke in two with a loud report at his Swan Island shipyard, I watched Kaiser's face as he received condolence over the long-distance phone from a close friend.

"*All* right," said Kaiser. There was a curiously don't-give-a-damn yet hopeful lift to those drawling words "all right." Then Kaiser comforted his worried friend. "You see, Jim, we'll learn a lot from that accident. We'll build better boats because it happened. We make progress by such disasters."

90

Lucky There Was Pearl Harbor

So too despite the perfidy, cruelty, tragic loss of life at Pearl Harbor, yet, taking the long view of it, that disaster woke up America, even including the complacent admirals. It stirred not only Kaiser but California's already progressive physicians to medical action that will become a model for the nation. It dealt a mortal blow to the medical economic fuddy-duddyism that threatened Garfield's health plan. So, looked at by the long view through Kaiser's optimistic spyglass, it was necessary, it was in some ways lucky that Pearl Harbor happened.

Two years before, in 1940, the San Francisco Bay cities of Vallejo, Richmond, and Sausalito were sleepy towns fairly well supplied with hospitals and doctors. They gave pretty good medical care to those who could pay. They were medically pretty charitable to those who couldn't. They did not dream of organizing to practice modern prepaid group medicine. Then came Pearl Harbor.

That triggered a mighty mass migration from all over America into California, and into these three no longer sleepy little cities. It was a tragi-comic reverse of the migration of the Okies a few years before. Then those wiry early-Americans were not wanted. But now the demands of war brought a far more immense migration not of Okies but of what you might justly call "Americkies" swarming from every state in the union in autos, jalopies, trailers, motor buses, trains, and hitch-hiking—all to be welcomed with huzzahs by airplane builders and shipbuilders hungry for manpower.

Yet existing facilities to house, feed, and medically care for this new migrant army—though so welcome!—were as

meager as those that made the condition of the Okies the
subject of John Steinbeck's great and bitter *Grapes of
Wrath*. When the god Mars reigns, then everything is for
the good of the soldiers. Then our leaders lose a sense of
proportion in their concern about the country's total population. This brings it about that the industrial army—
without which our armed forces would be absolute duds
as fighters—gets the leavings, of housing, of food, of doctors.

Under this human avalanche the population of Vallejo
quintupled in two years. Over Vallejo our finally frantic
admirals floated balloon barrages against possible Jap
bombers. But the teeming mass of new workers on the
navy's ships remained exposed to the actual and far more
deadly bombs of sickness.

Under Kaiser's mighty new shipbuilding, near-by Richmond mushroomed from its original 23,000 to a community of over 127,000 people. The Government was concerned about Kaiser's priorities for steel. It gave no
thought to doctors to guard the manpower of the builders
of his ships.

Over the Bay region there brooded medical chaos. Men
hurt in the battle to build boats had to wait days for necessary operations. Their wives, those lucky enough to get
into a hospital to have their babies, were forced to go back
to their homes—or hovels or what have you—within three
days after childbirth. Dr. A. E. Larsen, Medical Director
of California Physician's Service, reports that the doctors'
offices became miniature madhouses; appointments to see
a doctor often had to be made weeks ahead of time; in

hospitals there were frequently no beds available at all, not even for emergency operations. Vallejo physicians were forced to open wards in the dank and dismal basement of their hospital.

Dr. Larsen, tough and realistic young veteran in the care of medical have-nots that he is, deplores it that there has been no census of the suffering that happened in hovels, trailer camps, government houses because desperately overworked local doctors could not arrive in time or could not come at all. A U. S. Public Health Service officer records the sad saga of one Richmond mother. Her baby took sick. For three days with the child in her arms she wandered from the overcrowded office of one doctor to another, and from town to town. At last down the Bay in far-off Palo Alto she found a doctor with time to attend her child. It was a bit late. The next day the baby died from pneumonia.

Till August, 1942, Kaiser's workers suffered along with all the others. Then around the Richmond shipyards there began a medical miracle that compared well with the building of a Liberty boat in five days from keel to launching.

All over the nation, doctors, hospital authorities, officials of the U. S. Public Health Service who received frantic calls for help, all complained that the War Production Board would not allow priorities to build sorely needed hospitals in the new industrial areas. Now for their new Permanente Hospital in Oakland, Kaiser and Garfield got their critical materials. Kaiser convinced the

WPB in Washington with his always childishly simple but unanswerable logic—

You've got to build ships to win the war. You can't build ships without men. You won't keep up your manpower without men hurt and sick returned to health—in hospitals. These were absolutely as much a part of shipbuilding as were hammer-head cranes and steel.

Now at the Richmond shipyards six first aid stations rose with Kaiserish speed. Garfield staffed these with doctors, nurses, and first aid men as front-line soldiers against the disease and broken bodies of the shipbuilding army that was zooming toward 90,000 workers. The medical handling of the thousands of men and women, hurt and sick, has a tempo like that of Kaiser's shipbuilding. It is a rhythm of materials and men in motion.

At each first aid station there are ambulances and station wagons, plenty of them, waiting to rush sick or hurt workers to the Field Hospital, close by. Here the cruel red tape—and what pain-racked workman does not know it?—is cut to next to nothing. If they come as stretcher cases there is no delay at all. If they are hurt or sick but still walking, then they wait, but not too long, on comfortable seats before an extraordinarily long reception desk in a pleasant room.

Behind that desk there is a long row of young ladies, polite, solicitous, and not hard to look at. They do not dead-pan the workers with arguments and questions about their need or eligibility for treatment. They give all the benefit of the doubt. They route them to the Field Hospital's doctors with efficient speed.

Cases not suitable for care at Field Hospital roll, fast and comfortable, by ambulance to the Permanente Hospital 12 miles away from Oakland. For accidents records are established that dwarf those of the speedy building of the boats. One woman welder explained to my wife and co-worker, Rhea, how Henry Kaiser's god of speed is translated into super-prompt medical attention. At the shipyards this woman, Mrs. Rice, had fallen off a ladder and broken her pelvis. In agony of searing pain within 35 minutes she had come all that way by ambulance, had received her preliminary orthopedic examination by a surgeon whose hands, she said, were those of God, had been x-rayed, and was resting under pain-soothing opiate in her Permanente Hospital bed.

Mrs. Rice was nearly tearful telling how, instantly, at the first sign of pain's return, she had relief from the hospital's nurses and physicians. These are not on call by a button that you push for long in vain. You get them over an intercommunication system that brings quick answer from a nurse at a central desk.

Mrs. Rice had been herself a trained nurse on luxury liners before the war. She had seen and worked in hospitals in many parts of the world. She looked at all medical care with an experienced, a beady and a critical eye. Before the care she'd got at Permanente she lay dumbfounded. Nowhere in the finest private hospitals had she tasted better food. Nowhere had she seen such unlimited care as this she now herself received as a Kaiser worker.

This for her was the miracle: that such luxury, such concentrated attention, could actually be possible not for a handful of rich people with wherewithal to pay, but for 90,000 former medical have-nots. And at 7¢ a day.

She told her story convalescing in a two-bed semi-private hospital room. Here she could remain, not till she had no more money, not piling up an unbearable debt, not in danger of eviction because that bed was needed for another patient, but until the orthopedist determined that her treatment was complete. The room was cheerful, equipped with Venetian blinds to keep out the glare, air-conditioned, and decorated in an easy light green color. At Permanente Hospital all the patients are housed in such semi-private rooms. There are no wards in the old sense of that grim term. Private rooms are prescribed when the condition of the patient demands them, not because the patient happens to have the money.

This question of rooms versus wards, during the terrific expansion of enrollment of workers on the health plan, was a point of hot debate between Dr. Garfield and Henry Kaiser. The 70-bed Permanente Hospital had no sooner opened in late August, 1942, than it was deluged beyond its capacity by the Kaiser army swarming up from its original 25, to 50, 70, 90,000 shipbuilders. Sidney Garfield—it was his duty as a doctor—wanted to take care of them all, rooms or no rooms. Henry Kaiser—fanatical believer in a medical golden rule—maintained that if he himself should have a private room, then so should every worker, down to the humblest laborer or shipyard sweeper.

Garfield wanted to rent an old country club as an annex to the Permanente, turn one of its big halls into a hospital for the workers. Kaiser was indignant. "No, sir, we'll not hospitalize them in such barracks. It'll be a damned bull-pen," he said.

"Then we'll have to enlarge Permanente Hospital," said Sidney Garfield, with that quiet stubbornness for which he is obscurely famous.

Kaiser, you remember, had already signed a note at the bank for the original $250,000 for the building of Permanente Hospital. The institution had been in operation only three months. Now he came back to the bankers for $300,000 more, for a 100-bed addition.

"All right, Mr. Kaiser," they said, "and of course you'll sign this note, too?"

"No," said Kaiser. "I signed the first one in the interest of the health of this community. Now it's time for you fellows to get medically community-conscious too."

He got the $300,000 without his signature. It encouraged the bankers that, three months after the opening of Garfield's health plan, the original $250,000 loan was paying itself off at the rate of $25,000 a month!

CHAPTER 13

AGAIN THE GOOD
SAMARITAN

When he opened his health plan to the Kaiser workers, Dr. Garfield was careful first to submit it for approval to the leaders of the local medical society. He knew, of course, that prepaid group medicine was against their code of "ethics." But now they gave Garfield the green light. They had to. What else could they do? People were getting hurt, people were sick by thousands. Some were needlessly dying. Richmond and near-by communities had nowhere near enough hospital beds. It was utterly beyond the endurance of the local doctors to take care of the new human mass at the rate of one doctor for each 7000 people. They had no plan for group action. They left action to Garfield.

Garfield offered his doctors salaries that ranged from $450 to $1000 a month—not bad for a young physician or surgeon just out of hospital residency and facing the cold world of medical competition in individual practice. So, between August, 1942, and March, 1943, Garfield's staff at the shipyard first-aid station, the Field and Permanente Hospitals had grown to a group of 60 well-trained physicians and surgeons.

This medical team now set to work in these new hospitals which, down to the last gleaming item of medical, surgical, x-ray, and laboratory equipment, could compare with the best hospitals in the land. Now came happiness to these doctors. They did not have to wait in newly set-up private offices for patients who might have enough money to hire their expert services. They did not have to give charity to medical have-nots whom their hearts could not turn away—while their overhead for their equipment, their offices, their motor cars, their keeping up with the Dr. Joneses, was mounting. Under their ministering hands there now began to flow an immense stream of Kaiser's industrial casualties, and a far larger flood of workers afflicted with non-industrial ills that curse all humanity.

They rubbed their eyes in amazement at Dr. Garfield's new medical economics. His organization's total income came, 40 per cent of it, from payment by industrial insurance companies for workmen's compensation insurance medical care. The remaining 60 per cent came from the individual 50¢ a week from the prepaid health plan voluntarily subscribed to by the Kaiser workers.

Under this plan what could the doctors give the sick workers for their 7¢ a day?

On the preventive side, they could give all workers needing them the necessary vaccinations and inoculations.

For modern diagnosis of disease, there were basal metabolism tests, electrocardiograms, blood chemistries, and x-rays. Many prepaid plans limit the subscriber's allowance for this science—which is very costly—to between $15 and $25. In the Kaiser Health plan this science was lavishly on tap, with absolutely no hold-back because of its expense, but without question available when deemed necessary by the physician.

Garfield's doctors knew well that this scientific lavishness was not really extravagant. They knew that widely prevailing inability of physicians to give this "expensive" care is actually a nationwide false medical economy, devastating to our manpower, and profitable only to our morticians. . . .

In case of grave illness, insidious or sudden, whether pneumonia, a red-hot appendix, or heart or gall-bladder disease, or gastric ulcer, or cancer, Garfield's physicians, powerful as a scientific team, take the sufferers over with no qualms at all about their financial condition.

For his 7¢ a day, the worker gets complete hospital care, room, and excellent food—to a limit of 118 days for each illness. But this 118 days is purely theoretical. No patient is kicked out of hospital if his treatment demands that he must stay longer.

Skilled surgeons stand ready to perform major operations. If outside San Francisco or Oakland specialists are needed, these are instantly secured and paid out of the health plan.

There are no murderous extra charges for anesthesia, transfusions, medicines, or physiotherapy. This in contrast to many another prepaid medical care plan limiting the cost of operations and their accessories to sums such as $150. At the Kaiser hospitals there are no limits.

Insulin for the treatment of diabetes is furnished free. This is a feature hardly heard of in prepaid health plans. Workers are not preliminarily examined for venereal disease and excluded from Kaiser employment if they are infected. These ills are treated at no extra cost, till cured.

Ambulance service is provided within a radius of 30 miles. House calls are made by the Kaiser doctors without cost. In many plans the patient must pay from 50¢ to four dollars for such service.

Of course their excellent salaries, with no overhead, are a good reason for the notably high enthusiasm and morale of Garfield's staff of doctors. But there is a deeper cause for their spirit that you remark about them on their rounds of medical mercy to this great army of the industrially wounded and the sick. On a vast scale it confirms Sidney Garfield's discovery made in the desert. There and at Grand Coulee he had begun to be thrilled by what happened to his doctors when the cruel barrier of money was lifted from between them and their patients. Exit dollars—enter God.

Can it be that I have exaggerated this new spirit in Garfield's doctors? On this grave issue I must confess limitations as an observer, bitterly prejudiced as I am against any mere money consideration operating to hold back the hands of physicians in their mission of mercy to their patients. So the testimony of an able veteran industrial surgeon will carry far greater weight than mine. Let's ask for evidence from Dr. Carl A. Johnson, of Wilson, Oklahoma. When I met him at Permanente Hospital he had just finished three weeks of close study of the Kaiser health plan.

Dr. Johnson was far from a long-haired medical radical. During World War I he had served as a battalion surgeon, and there had won the friendship of famous Dr. Frank Lahey, past President of the American Medical Association. This friendship Dr. Johnson had retained, which he would have hardly done had he been a medical parlor pink. Johnson's working life had been spent as chief surgeon of the southern district of the Carter Oil Company in "Bloody Carter County" in Oklahoma.

He had the appearance of a hardbitten competent surgeon, the kind of man you'd instinctively allow to use his knives to enter the precincts of your own abdomen. His politics were far from those radical ones that would approve socialized medicine. He was a violent American Legionnaire. He had got his industrial medical experience the hard way, in a grim region where it is root, hog, or die, where you patch up and cure your patients because the Company makes money by its healthy husky manpower. Bright-eyed, lean-faced, thin-lipped, Dr. Carl A. Johnson was not what you would call a hare-brained do-gooder. His feet were on the ground.

A serious circumstance had brought him, worried, to inspect the Kaiser health plan. His son, also a physician, had joined Garfield's staff at Field Hospital. About the Kaiser health plan Dr. Johnson had heard nasty whispers among the doctors down in Oklahoma. Then, in Kansas City, he had got the opportunity to ask about Kaiser's medical care from one of the American Medical Association's political high command, a potent member of that invisible hand controlling the organized medicine of America.

The answer from this spokesman was devastating. Though Dr. Johnson does not say that these were the exact words, that answer was to the general effect that the Kaiser set-up was wildcat medicine, unethical in principle and practice, frowned upon by both the California Medical Association and the A.M.A. So immediately, worried about his son's medical future, Dr. Johnson had hurried West to Oakland. Garfield threw everything open to his inspection, told him to put on a white coat and work alongside the doctors of the Field Hospital staff.

Now this was Dr. Johnson's testimony.

"I've never in all my experience seen so much and such good care given for so little money," he said. "It's contrary to all my experience to see the blood chemistry, the electrocardiograms, and x-ray diagnosis—so limitless. X-rays? There's never a question asked about how many. And you know, those x-rays run into money!"

Dr. Johnson was astounded at the medically motley human material with which Garfield's doctors had to deal. "You understand," he said, "down in our outfit we don't take workmen over 45. We give them all a physical examination before they're employed. We weed out the unfit. That lightens our medical load tremendously. It cuts down our cost. And yet our men don't begin to get the complete care these Kaiser workers get."

Our veteran industrial surgeon couldn't get it through

his head how Kaiser could be doing his phenomenal ship-building with such a strange worker army. He had heard the prevailing jokes that anybody could get a job with Kaiser, that ballet-dancers, soda-jerkers, anthropologists, and philosophers were now serving as tin-hatted riggers, burners, welders, flangers. It was said, with grim humor, about Kaiser's industrial teamwork that men with good eyes but no arms were teamed up with strong-armed men who could hardly see.

"But you know," said Dr. Johnson, "at the Kaiser yards —with no physical examination—they take everybody, from 16 to 80. I've seen the staff treating men paralyzed down one side. Old duffers with heart disease come in, edema-tous, with their ankles swelled up and dropping over their shoes. The surgeons constantly operate on men with long-standing double hernias, stomach ulcers, diseased gall bladders."

Dr. Johnson explained that it was stipulated in the health plan contract that the 7¢ a day *did not* entitle workers to treatment for diseases they'd contracted before they came to the shipyards.

"But Garfield cheats himself," he said. "He treats them all. The staff takes care of epileptics, and lots of people with old chronic high blood pressure, and syphilis—and no questions asked. And the bad backs! You know that's the great stall of goldbrickers. But here every man's really sick till it's proven to the contrary. Elaborate orthopedic examinations. And x-rays? My God, the x-rays. Then even if they are maybe goldbrickers they give 'em physiotherapy and strap 'em up and send 'em back to work."

I asked Dr. Johnson if he thought this was foolish, whether it was too much of a muchness. "Hell, no," he answered. "They get 'em back to work."

But what most impressed our hard-boiled surgeon was the generosity of the health plan. "This is putting the whole practice of medicine on the spot. Talk about wild-cat medicine—contrary to ethics," he exclaimed, bitterly. "This is real Good Samaritan. Here you see the old Oath of Hippocrates—really in action."

CHAPTER 14

PRAISE THE LORD—AND PASS ANOTHER SECTION!

WHEN you set this epic medical generosity down in cold figures, then it's easy to understand Dr. Johnson's astonishment at the medical care the Kaiser workers can get for their 7¢ a day. If the none-too-healthy fighters of this industrial army had to pay for these services out of their own pockets, the total would often run to hundreds and even thousands of dollars. A check of the Permanente Hospital records, only four months after it had opened, showed 600 cases which, on a private fee basis, would have set the patients back between $500 and $1000; 40 cases would have run well over $1000; five over $2000. To cure one desperately sick girl worker of staphylococcus pneumonia the hospital disbursed over $7000 worth of treatment—including special nursing of three shifts a day for three months, for transfusions, for expensive drugs and serums. She lived.

What with a heavy percentage 4-F draft rejects, and

middle-aged, and old, and both men and women working outside in a foggy climate unaccustomed to industry's strain—the volume of treatments given the Kaiser workers is enormous. In the month of January, 1943, at the Field Hospital and aid stations, Garfield's doctors administered 116,285 treatments to this medically lucky shipbuilding army.

On this vast scale Garfield and his staff were demonstrating a revolutionary new medical economy. In the five months following the health plan's opening, the workers had paid $500,000 into the health plan; for this they had received the equivalent of more than $1,500,000 worth of treatment, when you estimate it on the fee-for-service system by which the individual pays his individual doctor.

But these are mere statistics; and figures do not cause revolutions. Talking to the hurt and sick men and women at the Field and Permanente Hospitals you sense the gathering storm clouds of a nationwide, momentous medical change. Here, for example, is the medical philosophy of Corporal Wilmer Patrick Shea—pronounce it "Shay." This Marine was a tall, tousle-headed boy with steady gray eyes set in a thin face marked with the chisel of long pain. He had had his right arm shot off at Cavite just after Pearl Harbor, and nearly died of hemorrhage and infection. Paid off as a Marine, he'd been pensioned at $80 per month for life—"if they don't cut down my disability when they find out how I'm working," he said with a faintly cynical smile.

"But so what," said Shea, "I wanted to really help build boats to take the stuff to our fellows out there. Believe it or not, they taught me to be a one-armed welder. Not what you'd call excellent. But I get by."

He went on to tell how one day he'd slipped on the deck of a landing boat, and broken his remaining arm, the left one. He'd been brought completely helpless to Field Hospital. The fracture was bad. "They kept me at the hospital longer than I thought they ought to," said Shea. "But that's the way they do everything here. They said they wanted to be sure this wing I had left would be absolutely okay."

Now with that arm in a sling he'd been back at his dormitory for three weeks, but had been coming back to the hospital for three excellent meals a day, fed him by a trained nurse. He had the run of the hospital, got to know everybody; and during this time our leatherneck had got an extraordinary insight into the fourth dimension of Kaiser's medical mercy.

"They don't bargain about the care you ought to get," said the Marine. "Look at the way they handle head injuries. Guys get clipped on the head. X-rays. No fracture. Most places they'd say *you're* okay. Go back to work. Here they take 'em in the hospital and put 'em under close observation."

It was funny the way they examine you for more than you think's wrong with you. "Take that guy, Brett," said Shea. "Hurt in an auto accident. Brought to the hospital and fixed him up—and then found he had a big cancer on the lip. Long before he'd come to work for Kaiser. Now he's been operated for that and is getting radium. All for his 7¢ a day."

The observant Corporal had caught the very heart of Garfield's prepaid group medicine: not cure, but prevention. "You see," he explained, "the way they treat us fellows at the shipyards keeps a lot of us from dying. Out of all the pneumonias, over half of them wouldn't have got any treatment if we hadn't had the health plan. And half of that 50 per cent would have died."

The Marine was correct in his statistics on pneumonia mortality, untreated.

"But at the yards they urge us to come to the Field Hospital," he went on, "when we've only got a sneeze and a sniffle and maybe a little fever. Then they don't simply give us a couple of aspirins and tell us to go back to work. They take us in. They x-ray our chests. At the first sign of pneumonia we're in bed and being treated with this new sulfadiazine."

Shea's testimony is borne out by the medical records. Of the last 105 cases of pneumonia treated at Field Hospital, only five have died. This figure compares more than favorably with the pneumonia death rate in the finest hospitals in America.

The observing Corporal had watched the intricate teamwork of the hospital group, every doubtful case going from the examining general physician for immediate and unlimited consultation by other doctors, and surgeons with special training, and then combed over from top to toe, chemically, and by x-ray. He showed he'd caught the economy of this lavish mercy. "Here's where these docs are different from the practicing doctors in their offices," he explained—

"Those docs have got to try to make plenty of dough off every sick man. Here they examine you carefully, and if you don't *need* an operation, you don't get it."

He said of course there are always gripers and gold-brickers in any outfit. "But there aren't many knocking this medical care, believe me," he said. Yes, he'd be glad to write out his opinion. His arm had been out of its sling for just one day. He had been practicing writing, southpaw. Now with his left hand he scrawled, a little wobbly but clear for all that—

"I as a shipyard worker think the Field Hospital and the health plan are tops. Because you get the best that science can give. I think the rest of the shipyard fellows feel the same." Signed—"Shea."

He handed it to me. Then his face, dead-pan and stern from the discipline of pain, lighted up into a sudden smile.

"I don't see why this can't be done everywhere, for everybody," he said.

Of the dozens of workers interviewed at Permanente and Field Hospital, all had different reasons for the happiness—not too common in hospitals—that they felt as they were convalescing. In one three-bed room at Field Hospital there were three women. Mrs. Culp, one month past a skull fracture, told how only a couple years before she'd had a serious operation that had set her back $450, for the hospital alone, not counting the doctor. . . . Now here she'd been in the hospital a month, with the most wonderful care, and not a sou to pay. . . . Mrs. Wilson, Negress—a leaderman at the shipyards—had been put to bed for a week for an illness to which doctors ordinarily would never have sent her to a hospital. And nothing to pay. She was going to tell all her people at the yards about it. . . . Mrs. Johnson, Dutch-American, face smashed and five ribs broken and talking short-breathed because of her pain. "This should be for every-body. We must organize and demand this not only for us workers but for all their families. It should be for every-body in America."

A burly workman recovering at Permanente said, "I never saw the kind of treatment you get here. They treat you so nice you hate to leave. Henry Kaiser's a big man but, by God, this is the best thing he ever did."

This patient was told that some top men in the doctor's union were off Kaiser for starting this health plan. "Let 'em try and stop it," he growled.

Talking to these witnesses you could read this in all their faces: pride that this was no charity they were getting. You could see they felt they owned this health plan. Pondering their unanimous testimony, you felt a tingle down your spine, a lift to make you forget the world's death and sadness. You knew that these people, and thousands like them, were going to be missionaries for medical justice. Here was the training ground for the leaders for the fight for a new medicine of tomorrow.

The truth of their testimony is proved by the Kaiser workers' mighty mass acceptance of the health plan, which is purely voluntary. Only one out of every five hundred offered it refuses it, and most of these rejects are due to the holding of some other form of medical insurance. 60,000 workers are already on the health plan's rolls; and all of Richmond's 90,000—with a trivial exception—stand ready to chip in their 7¢ a day, when the rolls are re-opened. This will happen when Henry Kaiser is sure that his expanding hospital facilities are ample for the care of his fantastically growing industrial army. It is one of Kaiser's limitations that he is a perfectionist, a medical idealist.

Meanwhile Sidney Garfield and his staff were practical. So, though only 60,000 of the workers were as yet allowed to put in their 50¢ a week, yet *all* of the 90,000—enrolled in the health plan or not—were being cared for.

How potent is this medical care in Kaiser's miraculous ship production? There are factors here that we do not know. We have not the figures, graphs, charts to show what part of it is due to the new rhythm of flow of ma-terials and men, and what part to the shipworkers' not being sick so long, and to their being returned to work so quickly after they are hurt or sick. Against the sneers and smears now sure to come, it would be well to be able to exhibit impressive graphs and figures. Neither Garfield nor Kaiser had them. In his free-swinging manner Henry Kaiser was sure that *some* part of the 200 per cent tumble taken in man-hours needed to build a Liberty ship, must be due to the workers' superb medical care. He left that to statisticians, and Garfield was so busy building hospitals and curing hurt and sick folks that there had been no time to collect them. It was enough for Kaiser at this moment that where any industry has installed good medical care, there has been formidable saving of manpower.

What most of all stirred Henry Kaiser was a hunch he

held. It could not yet be proved by graphs or figures. It was his hunch that their medical care was not the least of the reasons for a strange morale. It stirred the worker-army to a roaring chant of *"Praise the Lord—and Pass Another Section."* This was their battle hymn as they slammed and banged and hoisted and welded giant sections of Liberty boats together. This was their theme song as they built boats in days where they used to be built in months.

CHAPTER 15

NOT SCARED OF TOMORROW

YOU'D believe it unthinkable that there should be an attempt on the part of any American citizen to scuttle the bright promise of this immense experiment in the mass-healing of the human hurt and sick, in the saving of so much life. It was so effective. It was so merciful. And it was without question patriotic. Yet around San Francisco Bay there were medical whispers about the Kaiser health plan. They originated in medical sources that remain mysterious. They were broadcast by the medical grapevine through the coatrooms in the hospitals and after medical society meetings among the doctors. They besmirched Garfield's good name as a physician. They smeared Henry Kaiser and his health plan.

Our anonymous character assassins had taken a leaf out of the book of Hitler, who had pointed out that all associations of liars had long known the biggest possible lie the quickest to be believed by people. Sidney Garfield was falsely charged with having cleaned up $250,000 at the expense of Kaiser's men in their medical care at Coulee

Dam. The health plan at the Richmond shipyards was sneered at as "Garfield's peanut concession." As to Henry Kaiser's merit in it, the health plan was said to be a mere war baby. It was falsely said that the Permanente Hospital had been built with Government money, and not—as it actually was built—at the personal hazard of Henry Kaiser, backed by the half dollars of the workers.

These nasty whisperings gave Garfield sleepless nights. Not so much for himself. But the miserable lies were having their effect upon the morale of the physicians and surgeons of his staff. There is no respectability more exquisite than that of our dear doctors. To call them golddiggers, to compare them to peanut venders, is almost as awful as to put them in the infamous category of abortionists. The doctors of Garfield's staff were not members of the County Medical Society. If they applied, would they be admitted to the A.M.A.? It hardly seemed so. They were outside the medical pale. Now they began to be ashamed. Resignations threatened Garfield.

Now from the North came another threat, more tangible and more deadly than this cowardly campaign of lies. For their northern shipyards at Vancouver, Washington, Henry Kaiser and his associates had hocked themselves for hundreds of thousands of dollars for the superb new Northern Permanente Hospital. In some ways it surpassed the beautiful hospital at Oakland. Its surgeries, their adjacent work-rooms, the x-ray department and the laboratories had been planned by Garfield in a streamlined manner that was a model of super-modern hospital design.

For it he had assembled a staff of crack physicians and specially trained surgeons.

The grim need of this new hospital in Vancouver was not debatable. Yet the local doctors contested it. They were overwhelmed by the flood of new Kaiser humanity—workers, their wives and children. Almost overnight the population of Vancouver had jumped from 18,000 to 50,000. Now about the use of this house of mercy there began a controversy that could only be called idiotic if it had not been potentially tragic. Garfield had built beautiful obstetric and pediatric divisions into the Northern Permanente. He had planned to include the wives and babies of the workers in his northern health plan for the men. Now the local County Medical Society gave Garfield grim warning: Okay to take care of the men; hands off their wives and children! Though it was admitted that Vancouver's 15 local doctors were utterly unable to attend to the sickness and misery of Vancouver's new population of 50,000, now threatening expansion to twice that number.

Who in hell then *would* take care of the men's wives and children? That seemed to be a secondary question. They must not be taken care of by Garfield's physicians on a prepaid health plan. To enforce their edict the Vancouver doctors had a weapon. It was far more powerful than the lies and innuendoes circulating about the Kaiser health plan around San Francisco Bay.

This weapon was the possibility of putting doctors who were stepping off the reservation of medical "ethics"—into the Army. The Federal Procurement and Assignment

Service had the duty to gather physicians for our armed forces. Now the officials of Federal Procurement and Assignment, and its state and local boards were—most of them—also high in political power in the American Medical Association and its constituent state and local societies. Of course you see that fact's significance.

Here was the situation. The medical corps of the Army believed it was going to need the services of all young physicians, all men under 40, even including baby doctors and obstetricians. Now Procurement and Assignment had not the authority actually to draft the doctors as medical officers. But it did have a bludgeon. It could declare any doctor non-essential in civilian practice. And in that case, then such physicians, if physically fit, were 1-A for the draft, and liable to induction into the Army.

So, in addition to its patriotic function of getting doctors for the Army, it was also possible for Procurement and Assignment to use this power to make physicians of draft age toe the line of the code of "ethics" of the doctors' union, the American Medical Association. So now Sidney Garfield was given to understand that, so long as the physicians of Northern Permanente cared for Kaiser workers only, they would not be bothered but if they tried to heal the sickness of wives and children under an "unethical" prepaid health plan—well, then . . .

Down South at Richmond, California, Garfield's staff was also in danger of ruin, though not for this "ethical" reason. California was woefully behind the nation as a whole in delivering its quota of doctors to the armed forces. About the proportion of doctors the Army should have, compared to the number needed by California's civilians, it was not for the hard-working officials of California's Procurement and Assignment to decide. About California's tragic civilian medical situation it was not theirs to reason why. They could only obey Federal Procurement and Assignment, as it commanded from Washington. So now Garfield was warned that he would have to replace his medical staff with older men.

Thus in the autumn of 1942—it having just got fairly started on its career of mass medical mercy to 90,000 workers—it seemed the Kaiser health plan was doomed. Garfield faced this grim fact—

The scientific medical teamwork, the swift mending of smashed skulls and broken bodies, the rapid diagnosis and cure of early pneumonia, the expert healing of burned eyes, the modern management of diabetes, high blood pressure, and wrecked hearts, the surgery of appendicitis, perforating stomach ulcers, and the scientific treatment of cancer—all this could not be done with men whose only qualification was a plain "M.D." Garfield's health plan was modern group medicine or it was nothing.

Now Henry Kaiser himself came to the rescue of Garfield's threatened health plan. He joined battle with the invisible hand of organized medicine. He had the grim issue clear before him. The invisible hand sanctioned group medicine as it was so marvelously practiced—at the Lahey, Crile, and Mayo clinics—for people who had the wherewithal to pay. It was dead set against the development of Mayo Clinics for the common man.

Kaiser knew that he was not going to have to fight the

rank-and-file of America's physicians. If they were shown
how to do it, they would do their part to bring modern
medical mercy to all, to the least of suffering human
beings. Kaiser knew that he would not be opposed by
the doctors who composed the scientific medical *élite*.
They did not dirty their hands with medical politics. And,
finally, Kaiser was not awed by the power of the invisible
hand that held America's more than 100,000 physicians
enthralled. This was Kaiser's own power: that he was
scared of nothing. When he had hocked himself to build
the Permanente hospitals, he knew the hazard. He had
been warned that the war might suddenly end tomorrow,
and then he would be left to hold the bag. But the big
builder was not scared of tomorrow.

It is true that in this coming treacherous battle Kaiser
had a personal weakness. All his life he had been honest.
During those years when a kick-back was necessary to
secure a paving contract in Oakland, California, Kaiser
had simply not bid for such contracts. He was not at home
with connivers. In no walk of life did he talk the language
of the boys in the little smoke-filled room. To him their
double-talk was so much Choctaw. He underestimated
the power of political evasions, of skillful half-truths
uttered while a man looks you straight in the eye, of the
subtle and refined doublecross that is as common in the
despicable politics of medicine as it is in the corruption
of the politics of America's counties and its great cities.

Kaiser's weapon was the truth. In his faith in this he
was maybe too simple. With it our giant now invaded
Washington. He testified before a Senate subcommittee

on our manpower, where inquiry was being made into a current mystery. The enigma the good Senators were endeavoring to solve was this—

Why should our Army need one doctor, roughly, for every 100 of its husky young soldiers? While remaining American citizens—older and by no means so healthy—in many an industrial and many a rural region were left at the medical mercy of one physician for every two, three, four, even five thousand people?

This was the power of Kaiser's truth as he told it to the Senators, and so to all America. The most important single factor in all of our war effort was shipbuilding of which he, Kaiser, was the unquestioned leader and master. The wounds and the sickness of shipyard workers, if they are not cared for, mean guns that will not shoot, planes that will not fly, because ships will not sail—because the men who could have built them are sick, or disabled, or dead. And if the building of the ships was as basic to victory as the actual fighting, then it was just as important for his industrial army to be healthy as it was important for our front-line fighters. . . . And even more so—because such a great part of his shipbuilding army was 4-F, and old.

Kaiser did not ask that his health plan should be served by the ratio of doctors-to-men that were serving our soldiers. Dr. Garfield—brought by Kaiser to this Senate hearing—testified that the one-to-2000 proportion of doctors he was employing in group medical care, was ample. But Kaiser only asked that Garfield's team of doctors should not be raided.

Now to the Senators, to the newspaper reporters, to the spectators assembled, and to America, Kaiser let fly the devastating salvo of his truth—

"Dr. Garfield's position," testified Kaiser, "is that with the medical society practically directing and handling the Procurement [and Assignment] Service, if they are not in sympathy with our prepaid medical service—which some of them are and some of them are not, that is clear to everyone—but if they are not, then they are not the ones in any case to direct a service of this kind or to be associated with it. There could be prejudice and it shouldn't be there."

Kaiser then gave it as his opinion that the answer to the difficulty was an overall manpower committee—not dominated by medical politicians—"to procure doctors for the armed services and for the army of supply."

He did not blame the medical profession as a whole for the present deplorable medical mal-distribution. He did not blame Dr. Frank Lahey, past President of the American Medical Association and the head of the Procurement and Assignment Service. "Dr. Lahey is a fine man. I can't imagine a man more devoted and sincere and with greater leadership; it is the system that you are concerned with," said Kaiser.

And the system was in the power of the medical invisible hand.

Kaiser's testimony swept across the country on the front pages of the newspapers. It exposed the health plan's danger to what Dr. Herman N. Bundesen calls "the cleansing light of universal human knowledge." Immediately the

Journal of the American Medical Association made editorial answer. It must have amused all physicians who personally knew Kaiser. It must have interested those of his 90,000 shipyard workers who read it.

"Mr. Kaiser and other industrial leaders," said this editorial, "desire to maintain their individual empires without disturbance, regardless of the need of the armed forces for physicians."

Again Kaiser's answer sped across America. He addressed it not only to the people but to all their doctors.

"I am certain that the medical profession as a whole will not condone an unjust attack upon the motives and character of anyone who is devoting his entire energy to the war effort—and still greater, attempting to make provision for the sick and wounded, and not on a preferred basis, but on an equitable basis for all.

"We are trying to build ships—we need well men and women to build them, and where hospital and medical facilities have not been available, we have created them. If Dr. Fishbein is against our doing that, then I am against him," said Henry Kaiser.

So Kaiser spoke his own Magna Carta of medical democracy.

In California not only the citizens but many of the state's physicians knew Henry Kaiser, knew him not only for the great builder but for the honest and simple human being that he is. Now the response on the part of California's physicians to Kaiser's beam of the cleansing light of universal human knowledge was electric.

Headed by able and public-spirited Dr. Harold A.

Fletcher, chief of the State Procurement and Assignment Service, a committee of California's leading doctors crossed San Francisco Bay to inspect the Kaiser medical set-up. At Richmond and at Oakland they made close examination of Garfield's hospital facilities, of the character of his medical staff, and of the bookkeeping of the Permanente Foundation that administered Kaiser's health plan. They turned expert medical eyes upon this medical care that had been rumored to be wildcat, that had been denounced as "unethical" in principle and practice.

Here is their report, as published in the official journal of the California Medical Association—*California and Western Medicine:*

"An inspection of the Permanente Foundation facilities by qualified physicians has disclosed that an up-to-date medical service of unquestioned merit is being performed. Hospital and treatment facilities are excellent and a well-qualified and well-paid staff of physicians is available for any kind of medicine and surgery. From the standpoint of the present emergency and the rapid expansion in the Richmond area this complete industrial and health service is doing a necessary job which could not have been done nearly so effectively with the medical facilities existing when it was set up."

Dr. Harold A. Fletcher put it a bit more strongly to a group of California's leading doctors who met to plot ways and means of co-operation with Edgar Kaiser.

"Dr. Garfield and his staff are doing a hell of a good job with the Kaiser workers," said Dr. Fletcher.

So this group of leading doctors of California made

honorable amend for the earlier disparagement of Kaiser and Garfield; so they took the heat of the invisible hand off Garfield; so California's doctors joined with Henry Kaiser to save the health plan.

Now Dr. Homer Dudley and Dr. Ray Zech of the State of Washington's Procurement and Assignment Service visited the Northern Permanente Hospital. They too gave that hospital complete approval. This conduct of the California and Washington doctors bodes ill for the machinations of organized medicine's invisible hand.

CHAPTER 16

DEATH AWAKES THE
DOCTORS

BUT THERE was a flaw remaining in the mighty medical achievement of Sidney Garfield and Henry Kaiser. Admitted—it was astounding that Garfield within one year, starting from scratch, had organized the complete medical mercy for 125,000 workers at Richmond and Oakland, California, and at Vancouver, Washington. True—the Kaiser men and women were gathered into the largest cooperative health plan in the nation. Yet about it there remained injustice. It gave superb medical and hospital care to the workers but none to their wives and children. Of course Garfield had a good excuse. The Kaiser army had been growing with such speed that Garfield's hospitals, though also expanding in an Alice-in-Wonderland manner, had been able to bed the workers only. At the beginning of 1943 there was grumbling among the Kaiser men. . . .

What man who called himself a man could bear it to

take this medical care, good enough for old John D. Rockefeller himself, while his wife and babies were neglected?

Now the physicians of California came to the rescue. Their leaders had smashed a cruel taboo by going out of their way publicly to approve Kaiser's prepaid medical care. Now in this emergency where illness and even death itself threatened hundreds of thousands of women and children, the California doctors awoke. Through their California Physician's Service they believed they could undertake the care of this vast cohort of the medically forlorn. Dr. Ray Lyman Wilbur, the President of this service, put the doctors' duty in a nutshell:

"Communities on a prepayment basis can get the best medical care there is. If Kaiser can do that for the men, *we've* got to help bring the families along."

Wilbur's medical politics were simple. He had the passionate conviction that the care of the sick was the first flickering spark of real civilization. He saw the deep threat of their families' medical neglect to the shipyard men's morale.

"We can't permit this open sore between the man and his family," said Wilbur.

Though Garfield had removed the burden of the care of 90,000 workers from the physicians around San Francisco Bay, yet even so it was impossible for them to treat the hundreds of thousands of women and children. Dr. A. E. Larsen, Medical Director of the California Physician's Service, described the situation of the local doctors. "The heat on them was now getting so intense that doctors were actually running away from their practices in the Bay area," said Larsen. "They felt they were being killed, they were so overcrowded and loaded down. They'd come to the breaking point."

Now the California Physician's Service was ready to go into death-fighting action. Before Pearl Harbor, its organization by California medical leaders had got the California Medical Association into the doghouse with the invisible hand that ran the A.M.A. At the end of the 1930's the American Medical Association's official apologists were giving it out that things were pretty hunkydory with America's medical care. (This was unquestionable when you compared our doctoring with that of China, Chile, and Abyssinia.) These apologists announced the discovery, after an "investigation" that a relatively small handful, some 40,000 Americans, were being *denied* care when they were sick. (Would it not have been criminal if one raggedy child was denied it?) They gave no figures on the millions who were not denied it but were ashamed to ask for it as charity. They made no census of the millions who, on their slender incomes, could only buy medical science that was a travesty upon the scientific group medicine available to rich people at clinics like the Crile, the Mayo, or the Lahey. Their obfuscation that everything was medically hunky-dory was blown away by the scandal of scores of thousands of Americans yearly needlessly dying from cancer; by the infamy of hundreds of thousands of Americans infected with tuberculosis that remained undetected; by the existence of myriads malnourished, suffering a chemical hidden hunger; by failure to diagnose God knows how many people mentally sick but lacking new scientific treatment that could mend their brains if only it were given early; by the uncounted ones maimed or even dying from surgery that was inexpert or unnecessary.

Now our small band of California's doctors faced it. They were fed up with this medical infamy. They were ashamed of remaining medical ostriches.

The people of the socially seething State of California—they were the experimental guinea-pigs in America's greatest social laboratory according to Dr. Karl F. Meyer—were a bit crackpot, maybe, but they were not ostriches. They now were agitating a demand for state compulsory health insurance. Now their discontent together with the facts of needless sickness and death awoke California's doctors. These physicians determined that they were not going to be led around by the nose by the bureaucrats of any government, state or Federal. They decided that they would go into the business of mass medicine, but that they would run mass medicine themselves.

There was a bit of *noblesse oblige* about the medical leaders plotting their revolt against medical mossbackism and hypocrisy. Dr. T. Henshaw Kelly, a bulky fighting Irishman of San Francisco, was doing well in his own practice and why should he worry about the medical have-nots of the low income brackets? The same could be said of his friend, conservative, cool, and brainy Dr. Alson Kilgore. These two pioneers took expensive time off to organize California's new medical co-operative. They were lucky, early in the game, to find Dr. A. E. Larsen as the Medical Director of the California Physician's Service.

"Swede" Larsen—tall, sandy-haired and gray-eyed—was a Dane, dreamy but a fighter, visionary but with a Dane's remarkable genius for merging radicals and conservatives into effective human co-operation. In the last years of the 1930's, 4500 California doctors joined this Physician's Service to give prepaid medical care to doctor-less people in the state's rural regions, to groups of school-teachers and state employees, to a slowly growing mass of industrial workers.

The experiment was anything but beer and skittles. The patients subscribing to this new medical care plan had the right to pick out their own doctors, who were practicing individualistic medicine in their separate offices. There was no getting around the fact that good medicine— if you have to shop around for it that way—is frightfully expensive compared to Mayo Clinic medicine with groups of specially trained physicians and surgeons doing medical teamwork. In the beginning the actuarial calculations of this new mass medicine were cockeyed. On a unit treatment basis the doctors had been promised certain fees. They actually received only about half of what was promised and that griped them. The patients bellowed that this wasn't real prepaid medical care, that they were being gouged for all kinds of extras.

Yet, it was amazing, said Larsen, how the doctors stuck with it. "Their having to take reduced fees was a good thing because it made them suffer in the beginning," said Swede Larsen, "and without suffering at the beginning of a plan of this kind you lose the real guts of the whole thing," said Larsen, who is more than a bit of a mystic.

There was one good reason why the doctors were willing to suffer. Their plan was managed not by swivel chair bureaucrats but by doctors. Here was not the sinister little bug in the machinery that has made so many plans for government medicine ineffective. "Under government control the doctor is always suspected and the doctor is always wrong," explained Larsen.

"We interfered in no way with what the doctors wanted to do to their patients," said Larsen. "Here was the chance to make or break, to prove or disprove the honesty of a large part of the profession. I gambled on the theory that the majority of doctors are honest."

California Physician's Service did not tell any doctor whether he should or should not remove an appendix or cut out a youngster's tonsils. He did not have to fill out a government form for permission to give an enema. Yet over the co-operating doctors' medical conduct there now began a revolutionary supervision, an inspection by the doctors' own Ogpu. On punch cards designed to have a spot *for everything that could possibly happen between patient and doctor,* the chatter of business machines now began to accumulate a record of why and how and how much the California doctors were treating their patients— how much for what sickness. Here California Physician's Service invaded a sacred, a secret, a dark and sometimes bloody ground. The little punch cards issuing from the clattering machines began—for the first time in America's medical history—to expose the patient-doctor relationship that from time immemorial had been the doctor's own damned business. Larsen was in this a great medical pioneer, concerned not with the doctor-patient but with the doctor-public relationship.

The cold analysis of the business machines proved that Swede Larsen had been right to gamble. Experience with many thousands of patients, exposed to the medical mercy of almost every physician in the State of California over a period of three years, showed that between 90 and 95 per cent of the doctors were honest, that the vast majority of doctors are not gold-diggers.

Before Pearl Harbor these stumbling first steps in mass medicine by California Physician's Service aroused not much more than a faint nationwide medical amusement. After all only a few score thousands of California's medical have-not millions had joined this newfangled prepaid health plan after three years of experiment. Then came the pay-off. Now Swede Larsen and the doctors were set to meet the swirling human invasion that, post-Pearl Harbor, made California the medical hot spot of the nation. Now these physicians joined together with the Federal Government and these new citizens in an adventure in mass medicine unprecedented in the country's history. Now they began to silence these sniggers of medical contempt.

The workers and their wives co-operated in a roar of voices at their mass meetings demanding decent medical service that individual doctors could not give them and with which the Government had failed to provide them. The Government began to help through its Federal Public

Housing Projects. At Vallejo and Marin City Federal Housing managers added the cost of their prepaid medical care to the house rent of the tenants. This amounted to only $5 per month for an entire family regardless of size. It guaranteed complete care, including unlimited hospitalization and obstetrics. The California doctors, *not* the government, managed the medicine, furnished the doctors and the nurses.

The punch card story of his business machines showed Swede Larsen a simple trick for keeping an enormous case load out of the offices of the Bay region's harassed practicing physicians and surgeons. The breakdown of the figures accumulated from their three years of experience showed that the great bulk of a practicing doctor's work builds up from treatment of people for minor ailments, people who need to come for only two or three visits.

So now, at the housing projects, Larsen set up health centers. These were staffed by full-time, salaried doctors and nurses, on call day and night. When a man or woman or child falls sick, without thought of a doctor's bill they hurry to the Health Center physicians. Here they get their preliminary diagnosis and treatment, and nearly 90 per cent of the illness of the workers and their families can be taken care of at the Centers. The remaining more serious cases are routed by the Center physicians to the doctors and surgeons of the surrounding cities, and then to hospitals if their condition demands it. The doctors and the hospitals are paid on a unit fee basis out of the great fund collected, by the Housing Project managers, from the $5 monthly added to the rent.

Death Awakes the Doctors

No more than their patients do the doctors have to worry about the payment of the bills.

The hint of an epoch-making advance in preventive medicine is developing out of the device of locating the Health Center—that is to say, the doctor's office—right on the housing project close to the homes of the workers. This last winter, 1942-1943, there was a serious epidemic of upper respiratory sickness, with its attendant threat of deadly pneumonia. With colds and sore throats the workers and their wives and children flocked to the Health Centers for new science against this no-account respiratory sickness that can be so blitz-deadly, and that even in its lesser complications is the most formidable of all sappers of the nation's manpower. At the Centers the physicians gave them moderate doses of sulfathiazole. If the condition was deemed serious enough they were sent home to bed for a couple of days under the observation of the doctors and visiting nurses. The results?

While pneumonia has been rampant around the Bay region, while its death rate showed an ominous upswing in the nation, under this treatment there have been no cases of the deadly sickness among the grownups of the 5000 families living in the housing projects at Vallejo, and only three cases and mild ones among the children.

Swede Larsen is watching the figures accumulating from the scores of thousands of tell-tale punch cards from his business machines for the possibility of a glittering first consequence of California Physician's experiment in mass medicine. For it seems possible that when a patient—not held back by fear of cost—can go to a doctor who is convenient to his home, pneumonia may be better than cured. It may possibly be kept from happening at all.

Now the California physicians who grimly stuck by this mass medicine through its early financial disappointment, are beginning to feel a bit proud of their pioneering. The great bulk of the minor illness, now taken care of with promptness and economy by salaried doctors at the health centers, is putting the bookkeeping of the Physician's Service into the black. The fees per treatment, originally promised, are now paying off on the nose. The change of point of view of certain physicians about prepaid medicine was vividly expressed to me by Dr. Myrl Morris. She works full time, slogging up and down the muddy hills to take care of the ills of the children in the housing project in Marin City. This gallant lady had retired from a successful private practice of pediatrics among high-economic-bracket people. The war brought her back to this new service for the medical have-nots.

By her skill in nutritional science and a shrewd, conservative use of sulfa-drugs she had just fought through a serious epidemic of measles and scarlet fever among the shipworkers' kids, without a serious complication and without a death. This had awakened Dr. Morris.

"I used to be against prepaid medical care. I used to turn away from people who hadn't the money to pay me; I simply refused to think about them. I thought this prepaid medicine would cramp the freedom of doctors. But now I see it really works," said Dr. Morris with a bright gleam in her eyes.

The patients are not against this unexpected mercy.

The Physician's Service plan, like Kaiser's, is voluntary. At the Chabot Acres Housing Project at Vallejo, only 12 out of 3000 families have refused to pay the monthly $5 which is added to their rent for their complete medical care. Among the tenants are many Christian Scientists. All but four of these insist upon paying their additional monthly $5. Not that they use the doctors. But they come in, so they explain, "for the good of the community."

The California Physician's plan brings bright hope to industrial areas, nationwide, now so desperately short of doctors. Under the prevailing system where the bulk of the population is taken care of by individual doctors in their offices, it has been estimated that one physician can hardly care for more than 1000 people. Now in many communities, medically bereft, the number of citizens per doctor is reaching three, four, even five times that number. But California Physician's Service—concentrating the treatment of minor illnesses at its Health Centers and referring more serious cases to doctors in their private practices—finds that one physician can take care of 2500 people fairly effectively. And when an ample staff of visiting nurses is added, this may now rise to a ratio of one doctor for 5000.

This is the estimate of Mr. Brian Kelly, the genial Irishman and able medical statistician who presides over those business machines whose figures guide California's doctors in their experiment in mass medicine.

Successful in their care of thousands of workers' families at Vallejo and Marin City, California Physician's Service was eager to undertake medical mercy for the hundreds of thousands of wives and children of the Kaiser workers around Richmond. "We can't permit that open sore between the men and their families," said Dr. Ray Lyman Wilbur. There was no question that Health Centers, built on the Federal Housing Projects, could take care of the minor sickness of all these medically untended.

But for those who were more seriously sick, where were the hospitals?

Dr. Wilbur faced this stern issue. The California Physician's prepaid health plan could take care of the little sicknesses and pay the physicians and surgeons to examine and treat people in their offices. But it could not build the hospitals that have now become the heart of modern medicine. And Henry Kaiser would have modern medicine or he would have nothing. So it seemed as if the hope for co-operation with Garfield and Kaiser was stymied.

CHAPTER 17

MAYO CLINIC FOR THE
COMMON MAN

Could Henry Kaiser get them hospital facilities they'd need for the workmen's families? When California physicians began to ask that question they began to make medical history.

For, mark you, Kaiser would get them hospital facilities—medically revolutionary—or he would get them nothing. Facilities? That was not a drab word to Kaiser; it had a hint of the mystical. Facilities were more than the explanation of his giant building with a speed that seemed miraculous; they were the weapons he used to fight for a tomorrow when the golden rule would be universal. Facilities indeed! What were they for Kaiser? They were what kept too much sweat off a workman's brow. They were what kept kinks out of a workman's back and pains out of his joints. They were what gave the humblest men— controlling their switches and levers—a foretaste of that power that would one day make all men masters. They were what built useful monuments far greater than the pyramids with a speed and ease to make those tough task-masters, the Pharaohs, turn over in their mummy cases. Facilities were the reasonable mitigation of the curse of Adam; for all men still should work, that Kaiser knew. They were Henry Kaiser's obsession—from rubber-tired wheelbarrows to supermodern hospitals. They all had a simple aim: to cut down to a fantastic minimum the curve of man-hours to build a healthy and a happy new world of tomorrow. There was about Henry Kaiser a hint of old Prometheus in his ingenuity and generosity to provide facilities to lift the age-old, cruel, and senseless burdens from workingmen.

Kaiser was far ahead of the majority of physicians in his daring plans to provide facilities that would move men out of sickness and suffering back into work and health. His dreams were bold, maybe, but Garfield had shown him they were practical. If the California doctors wanted a hospital, it must be a new kind of house of healing, a health center where they could turn on the giant power of all the medical science now known. When I first met Kaiser in November, 1942, he said he believed the doctors would come along. Then I had doubted. But in December I heard him talk to a little group of Alameda County, California, doctors about the strange vision the new medical care of the shipyards workers had stirred in him. Those doctors were able, but most of them certainly not socially progressive. Kaiser rehearsed his medical dream on them at a dinner given by Dr. J. Louis Lohse, Kaiser's old friend and a fine but conservative surgeon of the city of Oakland. The air was a bit thick at the beginning.

"We've met," said Lohse, "to discuss how medical care is going to be prepaid and how it is going to be administered."

That was more than a mouthful to these physicians—it was TNT. In any guise it smacked of the bogey-word "socialized medicine"—the *bête noire* of doctors, the red herring dragged across the trail of all medical progress by organized medicine's invisible hand. These Alameda County doctors felt some kind of medical revolution in the air. They might even admit the need of it. But it was the bother of medical change that griped them. And who was Kaiser to believe himself its leader?

Then Kaiser began to paint his medical dream in simple words in a genial, patient, good-humored drawl. In his vision it was first of all explicit that the doctors must not be run by bureaucrats from Washington. They themselves must control their own medical science. There would be no invasion of their private practices among people *who could pay*. But there were millions—and what honest doctor denied it?—who could not pay for the best modern medicine. Not in the present set-up where the individual sick man has got to hire his hospital, his doctor. At the shipyards, *all* the workers hired any sick worker's doctors. And the simple reason the very best modern medical care was possible was that modern facilities were built round teams of doctors.

The workers—by their voluntary weekly 50¢ pieces—not only paid for their care, but built those facilities themselves. That was the big news. It ought to thrill you doctors. You don't have to get your facilities by begging them from the rich; you don't have to get them by Government handout.

Who'd manage the bookkeeping of this prepaid medical care? Industry, not the doctors, who don't pretend to be businessmen and admit it. Kaiser dealt his cards face-up across the table.

"We can show industry it can render this service without being responsible for the investment. This health plan's not an item of profit or loss. If we told industry it would be responsible for the investment, we'd fail," said Kaiser. But industry must be responsible for managing—with a voice in that management from the unions, from the workers who pay for their care, who really own it.

"But you, the doctors, have got to personnel it," said Kaiser. "You're the only ones who know how to staff it. You've got to set up the scientific standards, hold every doctor up to them. You'll have complete control of your personnel."

As Kaiser talked, the atmosphere, that had been very hedgehog, mellowed into an atmosphere of interest, of friendly curiosity. Kaiser got it across to the doctors that this was his credo: that they should run their own medicine; that prepaid medicine practiced by teams of doctors was inevitable and that it furnished the only chance for the common man to pay for his medical care. But what excited the listening physicians was that this new medicine could in a short time actually build and pay for its superb facilities.

Kaiser admonished them. Hadn't they been shortsighted to knock this health plan, to combat it? Now there was about him a bit of ancient Isaiah. . . . "Wash you, make you clean. . . . Learn to do well. . . . Relieve the oppressed. . . . Come now, and let us reason together. . . ." Here in California, in their own city of Oakland, the tremendous human migration had threatened medical tragedy, had caused medical confusion. Who had met the emergency? Garfield and his prepaid group medicine were showing how to handle it. Why should the local doctors oppose it? Why didn't they come along?

When those Alameda County physicians shook Henry Kaiser's hand good-by you could read in their faces that they had a new slant on the Kaiser health plan. And in the faces of some of them it was clear that they were stirred by its possibilities, its hope.

Now in March, 1943, only six months after the Permanente Hospital had opened, came evidence of the mighty economic power of Garfield's prepaid group medicine. The sum accumulating from the individual 7¢ a day from 60,000 Kaiser workers had not only paid for the upkeep and the lavish equipment of those hospitals. But, together with income from compensation insurance mandatory under California law, it was paying off the original sum advanced by Henry Kaiser for the building of the Permanente Hospital at a rate of $50,000 monthly. Within two years of that institution's opening, *the $550,000 needed to build and to equip it would be paid off in full.*

This super-speedy self-liquidation was new in medical history. It dazed ordinary doctors, accustomed as they were to practice in hospitals that were tax-supported, or wallowing, because of their high overhead, in a morass of debt. It drew indignant bellows of unbelief even from certain eminent experts in prepaid medical care. Their incredulity was based not on any examination of the Kaiser health plan's bookkeeping. It came from a weakness common to all experts.

In the words of Boss Kettering, "Because they hadn't done it themselves, it couldn't be so."

As in all works of genius, the causes for this seemingly miraculous self-liquidation of hospitals were simple when you broke them down. Dr. Sidney Garfield himself gives the lowdown on this high-speed amortization—

Hospitals have developed into the workshop of the physician. This work is specialized because the field of knowledge of medicine has become so extensive that no one man can master all. Yet, with all this division of work, instead of a hospital becoming one organized integrality, each division became a separate entity. This is in direct contrast to the organization that has occurred in the business world. Here the development of new methods and division of labor has resulted in an organization which usually houses a complete service under one roof.

On the contrary, in medicine as it is individually practiced there is enormous waste in facilities and equipment. Each doctor equips his own office more or less completely, whereas a group of doctors can pool its equipment and facilities to prevent duplication and economize in cost. For example, in individual medical practice, each doctor has his own laboratory and physiotherapy machine, et cetera. In groups, your doctors have one laboratory much more complete, and physiotherapy run by an expert.

Working as an individual, the doctor often tries to pass on problems outside his knowledge. Not only in medical problems, but in fee collecting, accounting, purchasing. In a group the opposite is true. Many an individual doctor still tries to do his own laboratory work because his practice is too small to enable him to hire his own laboratory technician or equip a good laboratory. He is wasting a good deal of his time doing something in which he is not well trained. In a group the doctors can afford to hire the best laboratory personnel.

Practicing individually, each doctor has to sell himself. This is obvious if he is to be successful. It results in the super-bedside manner which has no relation to real medical ability. In the group the *organization* is the selling point. For instance Mayo Clinic sells each doctor in the organization by *its* reputation. The doctor doesn't fritter away his time kidding John Smith by his bedside manner. He can devote his efforts to good medicine.

Individual practice doesn't permit ready consultation. The waste of the patient's time in going from one medical building to another for each speciality, is enormous. Consultation in a group under one roof is rapid, economical, and relatively simple.

Under individual practice the patient often sets himself up as his own diagnostician. He chooses his own specialist. He has persistent headaches and goes to eye doctors, brain surgeons, ear-nose-throat doctors—to wind up with the general physician who finds that he has hypertension. This results in a terrific duplication of cost and work.

Then there is the little item of the kick-back between one individual doctor and another. In a good group there is no duplication of doctor bills, and no fee-splitting.

Against the unquestionably greater scientific power and lower cost of modern group medicine, medical mossbacks moan about the disappearance of the sacred doctor-patient relationship. But when a man is really sick, what is more important—this tender chumminess or the quick use of the power of medical science? What kind of a pal of a patient can a doctor be, when he x-rays him in the dark, or operates upon his brain under deep anesthesia, or through a proctoscope studies the miseries of his bottom?

No, what the patient wants today is the knowledge not that the doctor has beautiful eyes and tender hands, but that he knows his scientific business.

Now here is what Sidney Garfield had organized for the 90,000 Kaiser workers who swarmed into the Field Hospital, and the Permanente. Not only did they have the pooled knowledge of the staff of highly trained physicians, surgeons, and laboratorians. But they had this team practicing under one roof, each specialist with his equipment at hand, each doctor convenient for instant consultation with another.

This medical teamwork was at the bottom of the notable financial success of the Lahey and the Mayo and other clinics. This was why, for their 7¢ a day, Garfield could give the Kaiser workers a Mayo Clinic for the common man. And build and pay off its hospital facilities.

What accomplished this pay-off with such dazzling speed was that final and simple economic trick that Sidney Garfield had invented long before in the California desert. He combined the industrial care and the non-industrial care in the same group of doctors. This concentrated the income from industrial compensation insurance and the health plan into a common fund. This brought the pay-off with speed that seemed so miraculous.

So now in March, 1943, the California physicians saw how Kaiser could build them the hospital facilities to take care of the Kaiser workers' families. Dr. Ray Lyman Wilbur, the President of California Physician's Service, was not among those experts who, because they have not done it themselves, disbelieve and look a gift horse in the mouth. At the first conference to plan this momentous co-operation between the California doctors and Henry Kaiser, Wilbur congratulated Garfield on his pioneering. "It's the facilities that now dominate modern medicine. Grouping your staff under one hospital roof, you've compelled them to work around those facilities. Your doctors aren't working for the automobile company or the chauffeur or the real estate agent or to keep up to the social standing of the Joneses—they're working for the Kaiser workers," said Wilbur, with a smile that he permits himself upon rare and important occasions.

Here now Wilbur, medical statesman, saw the bright promise for unprecedented co-operation between doctors, and Kaiser, and the common man. For when the Permanente Hospital was paid off, as it soon would be, then great profits would begin rolling into the Kaiser health plan. Profits, yes—but not for Henry Kaiser. Because, you recall, the health plan had been set up not for profit, but as the Permanente Foundation. And the money accumulating could now overflow—for the building of the needed hospital beds for the workers' families, and to pay the members of California Physician's Service who will cooperate with Garfield's doctors to care for those families, and for vast new developments in community public health and industrial medicine.

April 9, 1943, at Henry Kaiser's home in Oakland there was a conference. It deserves to be noted and remembered by America's medically forlorn. Dr. Harold Brunn, world-famous chest surgeon from San Francisco, was there. An honest man, he deplored the bankruptcy of ideas for progress that marked organized medicine's invisible hand in today's medical crisis. Brunn was no medical pooh-bah remotely authoritative because of those mystic letters, M.D. He was looking toward Henry Kaiser, graduate of the seventh grade, as a medical leader.

Ray Lyman Wilbur, Chancellor of Stanford University and past President of the A.M.A., honored Kaiser by his presence. He was likewise not medically authoritative or snooty. He was dour in outward manner but with a great doctor's heart. Wilbur understood this medical qualification of Kaiser's, that had been written about him many years ago by Leland Cutler—

"Builder that he is, I think he has not ever crushed a flower half-hidden in the grass that he did not wish he might have walked some other way. He has not built upon the ruins or the wreckage of his fellowmen, nor erected selfish slabs of structured stone to glorify himself."

Kaiser's old friend, Dr. Louis Lohse, conservative, came too, that evening, to show his willingness to follow non-medical Henry Kaiser in his revolutionary medical adventure.

Swede Larsen of the California Physician's Service and Sidney Garfield were there to work out the details of this projected historic co-working of the medical profession on the one hand and industry and labor on the other.

That evening the plan of campaign of this co-operative death fight was drawn up tentatively. California Physician's Service would undertake the medical care of the workers' wives and children. The payroll deductions for the family plan would be managed, as with the workers, by the Permanente Foundation. The health centers on the Kaiser housing projects would be staffed by Physician's Service's doctors and nurses. The Permanente and Field Hospital facilities would be opened up to any dependent entitled to care under the plan who is receiving treatment from any doctor of the Physician's Service, whether a member of the Permanente staff or not.

The doctors of Garfield's Permanente staff were to be invited to become members of the California Physician's Service. In short, the Kaiser physicians were to be taken into organized medicine's sacred precincts. Such were the terms of the proposed momentous union. The benefits of this alliance of industry and medicine were unquestioned. The California Physician's Service members would enjoy the advantages of the Kaiser health plan's mighty power to

build hospital facilities. It would expose individually practicing doctors to group medicine. Garfield's doctors would
become medically respectable, and have free interchange
of science with the cream of the medical profession of the
San Francisco Bay region.

That night was born the promise of a model for the
community Mayo Clinic for the common man. Let it suc-
ceed—and how could it fail?—and it would spark the for-
mation of thousands of such death-fighting organizations
from coast to coast.

CHAPTER 18

DOCTORS FOR TOMORROW

HENRY KAISER believes that we can begin right now to build these Mayo Clinics for the common man, wherever there are industries. Even where the industrial units are small, their managers and their men can pool their efforts to build health center hospitals that can be used in common. He is a great believer in good, not cutthroat, competition, and thinks the new prepaid group medicine will be stronger if its units are kept small.

"You can't centralize 135,000,000 people," says Kaiser. "You haven't got the force for the remote control. You can't run medical care from Washington. But if you could establish, let's say, 1000 such health centers, then you'd really begin to serve the people."

As he drawls those words, 1000, you see the builder's gleam in Kaiser's eyes. He throws out that number arbitrarily. He does not stop to quibble with timid authorities who want to make old hospital facilities do. He does not argue with hospital "experts" about whether it is 1000 or 500 or 50 new hospitals that are needed to build a new vigorous America. Statistics about the number of hospital beds we already have do not impress him. Nor do they fool him.

He knows the kind of hospitals that make up the impressive number of hospital beds credited to our nation. He knows that there are many good hospitals. He also knows about hospitals that are dirty reeking dens that remind you all too well about how short a time ago hospitals were poorhouses. He knows about so-called hospitals, not recognized by the A.M.A. About sinister institutions, "private hospitals," where certain high-powered surgeons ply their trade. Here they cut out tonsils, appendixes, thyroids, wombs, and gall bladders—not so much for the sickness of the patient as for their own remuneration.

Kaiser is not thinking of medicine as it is practiced today. He sees America, urban and rural, dotted from coast to coast with new hospital health centers where groups of doctors give people the power of medical science, all that science to all the people.

Where will management, labor, citizens, and the doctors—in short where will our communities get the money to start their new health centers?

For the most part from the local bankers, just as Kaiser himself got it at Oakland for the Permanente. The bankers can be shown that when these health centers are well managed and well staffed, their financing will be covered by the soundness of the investment. The paying off, the amortization, is produced by the health plan members, the users of the hospitals.

But, despite the brilliant financial success of the Kaiser

health plan in California, let's admit it may be difficult to convince many bankers. Let's grant that many of them may be leery of taking *all* the risk. Then, says Kaiser, the local bankers can take part, let's say, 50 per cent of the loan. The balance of it could be guaranteed by the Government. Just as the RFC encourages and stands back of industrialists with sound plans to build plants to produce cement or magnesium or steel.

Kaiser knows there are medical care authorities who object that communities can finance the new health center hospitals only where there are vast payrolls from great masses of workers. Already there are "experts" who lament that the Kaiser health plan is a mere war baby.

To these Kaiser gives a devastating answer. The Grand Coulee hospital paid itself off within three years, though Garfield and his group of doctors were handling a load at its peak of only 5000 workers and their families. And their pay was not wartime boom pay, but moderate. Garfield has calculated that community groups of 2500 people can build, support, and pay off their hospital facilities.

Then there are other "experts" who wail that this may be all right in cities, but that it will be no go in rural regions where farmers notoriously have not got the ready money. Again Kaiser has the answer. The economic power of health plans of industrial regions is a tremendous one. When the hospitals there are paid off, then they will make formidable sums of money. . . . And this money can then overflow—with urban and rural citizens co-operating—to build small hospital health centers in rural regions.

But the authorities, the gloom-boys, have a last objection. What about remote rural regions, far from industry? Already it has been demonstrated that even here the building of a hospital will pay itself off, when the prepaid health plan is well managed and the hospital is staffed with doctors who are centralized and work on good salaries. Led by a tough and brave man, Dr. Michael Shadid, the farmers of southwestern Oklahoma began a co-operative health plan in the grim depression years of the early 1930's. Shadid and his doctors had the bitter and powerful opposition of organized medicine's invisible hand. The farmers had God himself against them in those dry and dusty years of the middle 1930's.

Today Dr. Michael Shadid and the farmers are proud of their Elk City Community Hospital. They own it free and clear, lock, stock, and barrel, with a $70,000 surplus in the bank.

Kaiser knows that the nation's new health center construction will make up a substantial part of the giant building that is going to give us a new America. He knows that the time to start to plan is now. He is happy that our Government has already removed the worst of the obstacles to the spread of nationwide group prepaid medicine. The Supreme Court decision on January 18, 1943, when it confirmed the conviction of organized medicine's invisible hand for its conspiracy to block the Washington Group Health Association, at the same time affirmed the right of the American people to seek decent health security. It removed, so says an editorial in the newspaper, *PM*, "the threat of economic terrorism and social ostracism which has hung over American doctors who dared to participate in group health plans frowned on by medical monopolists."

Industrial managers are now beginning to visit Dr. Garfield to study the Kaiser health plan in its spectacularly successful and financially powerful operation in the states of California and Washington. Not only the progressive California physicians, but other leading doctors are making pilgrimages to this new medical shrine built by Sidney Garfield.

One of these is Dr. Arthur C. Scott of Temple, Texas. Dr. Scott—Texas Scott to you—has long been head of the excellent Scott and White Clinic there. This is known as a miniature Mayo Clinic in the Lone Star State. Texas Scott has an outraged sense of medical justice. He cannot get it through his head why, if the rich man can *individually* pay for group medical care, then why can't the common man pay for it jointly?

Now Garfield has shown Scott how it can be done. And Scott is impatient, even impetuous, like Henry Kaiser. He believes industry, labor, all citizens, and the doctors should begin nationwide planning *now*. He suggests that the Federal Government should set up a medical loan agency, a medical RFC if you will, to encourage local bankers.

CODA

In the health centers that we now can build, Kaiser the master builder sees the foundation for a new American humanity. He is a dreamer but realistic. He does not kid himself that we are "an essentially healthful America." He knows about the 40 per cent of our boys who are 4-F rejects from the draft, a large part of them physical wrecks because they never did have decent medical care. He has seen the brave but pitiful army of his own workers, scores of thousands of them a human flotsam and jetsam because medicine has not known how to distribute the power of its marvelous science. This sad spectacle enrages Kaiser. He knows that the human adventure is only in its morning. He knows that the faith and courage needed to pursue it can come only from a strong, vigorous, and long-lived humanity. He gambles that the law of work, health, and peace will triumph over today's law of blood and death.

His heroes in tomorrow's new fight for life are the doctors. He looks forward to the return of a vast commando force of young physicians from the army. They are no longer enthralled or misled by the reactionary double-talk of organized medicine's invisible hand. They have practiced group medicine, *good* medicine, upon the soldiers and they know its beneficent power. Already they are laughing at the horse-and-buggy individualistic medicine of yesterday.

The new hospital health centers will be the workshops where the power of the science of these young men will begin to work a fantastic transformation upon our nation now living, so large a part of it, half-alive. The great economic power of the new prepaid medicine practiced in these health centers will give a new lease on life to our older doctors, too. Joining these health plans as the California physicians are now joining Kaiser's, there will be the wherewithal for them to become re-educated, to become teamworkers happy that they, too, can join in the group medicine of our new fight for life.

Kaiser is a genial giant, and optimistic. He knows that the time has come when we should no longer bear our misery with a smile. The time has come for medical science to make us laugh and be happy. This is his vision—

The medical mercy of these workshops can now rapidly wipe out the curse of syphilis. It can cut the present death toll from cancer by more than one-third. It can begin to conquer the rheumatic heartwreck that saps the strength of hundreds of thousands of our young people, the heartbreak that yearly kills them to the number of 40,000. It can abolish the misery and the insanity of women's change of life. By the skilled use of the new powerful hormones it can extend the sexual activity and lengthen the vigorous prime of life of men, so that we will no longer say that we grow old too quick and wise too late. It will abolish the prostate gland misery that makes so many old men social outcasts. It will wipe out tuberculosis with a speed that will frighten the executives of the National TB Association. This new group medical mercy will sound the death knell of still murderous lobar pneumonia and will remove the strength-sapping infection of gonorrhea from men and its maiming curse from women. In the new health centers our physicians and chemists will uncover and correct the widespread chemical hidden hunger, the vitamin starvation that gnaws the nation's nerves and weakens its muscle. Here too the new shock therapy will be turned against early mental sickness—to rob our asylums of hundreds of thousands of their tragic victims. Practicing physicians will co-work with eye specialists to check the blindness of glaucoma in its beginning. With all science instantly available, the doctors of these new hospitals will cut the death and maiming of newborn babies to a low that will excite the envy of Dr. Herman N. Bundesen—greatest of all fighters for the lives of children. And this community group prepaid medicine, freeing doctors from economic pressure, will cut down the pitiful toll of maiming, and of death, that exists because of surgery that is remunerative first and curative afterward.

Kaiser knows that this giant upsurge of human strength can begin, thanks to the power of known medical science already in the hands of our doctors. But the "profits" that will roll into the health plans after they have amortized their hospital health centers will be used for still more glorious medical adventure. He knows that today our medical research is going ahead on less than half-throttle. The funds that used to support it from the largesse of the rich are dwindling. The money allowed research by our State and Federal governments is uncertain, and its grants are continually in danger from legislative budget-slashers and economy howlers. But now the profits from group prepaid medicine will give our questing death-fighters powerful new sinews for their war.

Not dominated by Government bureaucrats, not having to cadge favor from the strange beings who dole out research money "to the right kind of men" from our eleemosynary medical foundations, the doctors in our new hospital health centers can be scientifically independent, can plan and do their own research. Here they can begin a new assault upon those great diseases that yet remain inscrutable and enigmatic. You do not find all your Leeuwenhoeks or Pasteurs among the white-haired medical boys supported by the National Research Council or the great foundations. You will find more of them where you now find your aviators and commandos and where you've always found that human salt of the earth that makes up mankind's pioneers.

Kaiser knows that the science that will now be possible, thanks to the financial independence of the new hospital health centers, will tap a now latent, hidden research genius. It may be in Oskaloosa, Iowa, or Corpus Christi, Texas, or Fontana, California, that our new teams of doctors will unlock the chemical secret of multiple sclerosis, of epilepsy, of inoperable cancer, and of that mysterious deterioration of our hearts and blood vessels that helps to kill us in mid-life and that helps to make us old while we should be in our prime.

Kaiser does not believe this new fight for life must wait till some peaceful tomorrow. Large industries, groups of small ones, groups of doctors today left at home, the labor unions, the farmers' organizations—all should band together now to demand the government Medical Loan Agency. This would guarantee to the local bankers 50 per cent of any losses which might come as a result of the banks' willingness to finance these new Mayo Clinics for the common man.

Then for tomorrow Kaiser sees a still brighter promise. "How shall we reward the scores of thousands of young doctors who've risked their lives at the fighting fronts in the war?" he asks. "Death has awakened these doctors.

"We should urge that the Government provide them with an extra compensation, and special encouragement for the health centers that they will be ready and anxious to organize. The Government might well guarantee these returning doctors not 50, but 80 per cent of the cost of building their needed facilities."

That's why there's a gleam in his builder's eye when Henry Kaiser draws his sweeping blueprint of the new health centers. He is only a contractor, maybe, and the steel and concrete and light metal alloys growing with a banging, clanging rhythm into the new hospitals will be a pleasant music to him. But he sees beyond the steel and concrete. In the long run Henry Kaiser will have his share of our remembrance as one man who did his bit to build the doctors, and not only the doctors but the human beings of tomorrow.